GEEK'S GUIDE

TO BRITAIN

The Register's travel guide to Blighty's places
of invention, creation and technological wonder

First published in 2016 by Situation Publishing Ltd.

ISBN 978-1-5262-0236-9

Editor: Gavin Clarke
Design: Fenke Fros

Situation Publishing, The Register, 12-16 Laystall street, London, EC1R 4PF

Contents:

Destinations

Introduction

We were pounding down the A12 in Suffolk when I had my own, personal Geek's Guide to Britain epiphany.

A cold, Sunday December morning, we were en-route to Snape Maltings – two families in a convoy of two vehicles - to see Father Christmas land by sail barge.

We'd paused at a roundabout when my mate in the lead car wound down his window and pointed - but he didn't need to. I'd already seen it.

Rising above the flat and frozen land: BT Adastral, near Martlesham Heath.

There's no mistaking BT Adastral: a tower topped by a square knocked off kilter, like a gigantic set of building blocks from Corbusier, diligently placed but then subject to a glancing blow in the rush to tea time.

There's no mistaking its significance: the home of UK broadband, according to BT who owns it, and a place insiders claim houses enough high-powered telecoms and computer gear to run a country the size of Belgium. Its long association with technology stretches back long before the digital age to the Royal Flying Corp in the First World War.

No mistaking BT Adastral.

And, no entering it: Adastral Park is off-limits to the casual visitor.

And that was my particular Geek's Guide to Britain epiphany: a nation's rich engineering and technology heritage, hidden in plain view.

Returning to work in January my fellow Reg writers recounted similar tales from across the UK – radio astronomy sites, former radar bases, lift testing facilities, lost nuclear bunkers - places also waiting to be celebrated.

A series was born.

Britain is a country of inventors and problem solvers, people who've tackled challenges big and small through the medium of science, technology and engineering. Their legacy: factories, facilities, bridges, tunnels, bunkers - and more. Some still in action, more than a century after their creation, and others gone.

What if we explored such places? Toured behind the scenes of those that are off limits? Explored locations long-since bulldozed by developers?

What if we could chart places you might otherwise drive or walk past? Turn them into an afternoon or a weekend travel destination for you - and the family?

Geek's Guide to Britain is that series.

But, there's more.

Researching Geek's Guide to Britain revealed something unexpected: museums and associations around these destinations that, together, form an ecosystem.

They are run by individuals or groups, outside the museum super league. Generous of spirit and time, they bring deep knowledge of subject – and often direct personal experience – of the technologies and stories that they are dedicated to keeping alive. Places where kids can scramble around old hardware or press buttons on the radar systems that helped keep Britain safe during the Cold War.

Geek's Guide to Britain aspires to their ideal: not to just observe Blighty's places of invention, creation and technological wonder from behind glass - but to get hands-on.

It's an approach we think the nation's founding boffins – hands-on people themselves – would have approved of.

Gavin Clarke
Editor, Geek's Guide to Britain

Jodrell Bank
Cheshire

Joe Fay

GEEK'S
GUIDE
TO BRITAIN

Reg man goes time travelling at iconic observatory

Jodrell Bank: the visitors' centre at the start of the Universe

There are two ways to approach Jodrell Bank. From the north you fly through the WAGish end of Cheshire, with towns such as Wilmslow and Alderley Edge housing Manchester and Liverpool's finest and their harems. I prefer coming from the south, under the Twemlow Viaduct, a 105ft (32m) high, 500 yard (457m) long symphony of red brick, completed in 1842.

The road dips here, so that as you come under the bridge, you tend to hit the accelerator, before levelling out just in time to start catching glimpses of the Lovell Telescope across the fields as the road wobbles its way towards Macclesfield.

It's still eerie, suddenly seeing the dish pop in and out of the lines of trees carving up the tweedily rough North Midlands countryside. It's as if the credits for countless popular science shows were being projected around you. You're on Jodrell Time.

If we all know what the iconic Lovell Telescope looks like, some of us might be a little fuzzy on what it's for. To recap, its day job is to observe the Universe in the radio spectrum, and one of its early successes was in unlocking the secrets of quasars. But it also played a major role in the Cold War's space and arms races, tracking the Russians' first space shots, conveying instructions to US space probes, listening in to traffic from Russia's probes and standing by to track incoming Russian ICBMs.

Radio Astronomy began at the site in the late 1940s, when the University of Manchester's Bernard Lovell got sick of interference in the city, and hauled his collection of Army surplus radar kit to the Uni's out-of-town botanic gardens. He wheeled, dealed and otherwise pushed through the construction of the 250ft (76.2m) Mark 1 dish which now bears his name. At the time it was the world's largest steerable radio telescope. Six decades on it's still probing the Universe and is still the third biggest steerable 'scope - on this planet, anyway.

A few years back there were rumours that the site was for the chop. Staffers at the site tell us that was never really on the cards, as any decision would have been based on peer review of the science it produced. And on a pure science basis, Jodrell had a pretty strong case to continue its work. Quite apart from collective affection for the iconic site, Jodrell Bank is ground zero for the UK's eMerlin project, which links the Lovell Telescope with six other UK-based radio telescopes, to give a unified dish array spanning 217km. It would have been difficult to argue it was not producing world-class science

Arguably more important for the site's future, Jodrell is also the project HQ of the Square Kilometre Array (SKA). This €1.5bn project will run a network of thousands of radio receptors across Australia and eight countries in Southern Africa, equating to a radio telescope dish one kilometre square. When it's up and running, it will be generating a bracing 960,000,000GB of data a day.

But these days it's not just enough to be relevant. You have to demonstrate it. Scream it, even.

And so things have changed a bit. The Jodrell Bank Centre for Astrophysics - to give it its full name - is not just a world class science site with a visitors' centre. The site has had a major makeover, and acts as the backdrop for the Beeb's pop astronomy *Star Gazing Live* strand, runs a comprehensive programme of events to evangelise for astrophysics, and even hosts music festivals.

Some of us might have memories of just pitching up to the site, wandering in from the car park and having a couple of sandwiches under the dish, perhaps contemplating our role in the cosmos, or simply trying to remember what we were doing at the family wedding we'd attended in Wilmslow the night before.

Today, a tasteful wooden wall prevents access to the site from the car park. You can wander into the Planet Pavilion's cafe and view the site from there. But if you want to enjoy the full visitor experience, or if you're a groupie trying to get to *Stargazing Live*'s Brian Cox and Dara O'Briain, you're going to have to cough up £7 for an adult or a fiver for a kid. A family ticket - two adults, two kids - will set you back £20. (The proceeds all go to the centre's education activities.)

Incidentally, the cafe is really rather good. Good enough that the designery ham sandwich and chips we had almost completely obliterated the disappointment we felt that we'd missed the full English by a matter of minutes. (11.30 local time if you're wondering, but be warned each of the array of clocks on the wall shows the time on a different planet in the solar system.)

The Planet Pavilion packs in a quick intro to space, with lots of astral lighting. And a shop. That relief pattern across the front of the building is actually a radio map of the Universe, created at Jodrell Bank, and the motif is repeated throughout the park, reinforcing Jodrell Bank's pivotal role in mapping the cosmos.

Things get more detailed in the larger Space Pavillion, with plenty for kids to prod, listen to and grapple with. You can listen to the sound of the Big Bang, and then explain it to the kids. You can fondle a meteorite. Despite quite clearly being a lump of (mainly) iron this was strangely awesome, coming the week after the Russian meteorite shower.

You'll want to get the kids into the Science Show, and the Ask an Expert Session, which gives them the chance to discover there are real astronomers who are not Brian Cox. Or even Dara O'Briain. With about 150 on-site, and more to come as the SKA project spins up, you're unlikely to get the same expert twice, even if you buy the full year pass at £60 for the basic family version. The sessions can go with a bang, literally, but we won't spoil the surprise here.

What you don't get in either of the pavilions is a lot of history of the site or Bernard Lovell, the telescopes' early successes in identifying quasars and pulsars, not to mention tracking the US and USSR's jab-trading in the space race, and its role as part of the UK's ICBM early warning system. This may seem unusual for something that is both Grade I listed, and a candidate for World Heritage Status. This is a conscious effort on the part of the team running the site these days, with the urge to carry out cutting edge science and act as a beacon for budding physicists trumping the temptation to lapse into the comforting arms of the UK heritage industry.

Still, the history is covered reasonably comprehensively as you walk around the telescope itself. When we visited, it was whizzing around like a cosmic taxi driver's head. Older than most *Reg* readers, it's still the world's third-biggest moveable telescope. In fact, it's moving all the time to compensate for the Earth's rotation. Having 3,200 tons of metal and railway bogey noisily spark into life just as you're contemplating your place in the Universe can be disconcerting.

Almost as disconcerting is the ever-present threat of foam, air-powered rockets. The site is riddled with them, part of the drive to give younger visitors a hands-on chance to play around with Newtonian physics.

If you want a break from the cosmos or the kids, you also get to walk around the University of Manchester botanical gardens - the botanists are still here. As part of the makeover, there's a new Galaxy Garden. We didn't get to see the garden though, as we were treated to a rare behind-the-scenes tour with Jodrell's associate director Dr Tim O'Brien.

If the telescope itself takes us back through eons in space, a walk around the backrooms at the site will catapult you through a history of computing since the 1950s.

We had a walk through the control building for the Lovell Telescope. If you were at college in the UK anytime before 1990, you'll be familiar with the 50s-style academic architecture. The control room itself felt similarly familiar. At first glance it looked like a set from a 50s sci-fi classic, or a particularly well-funded episode of Doctor Who. All steel-grey chassis and post-war municipal functionality.

All in all, it's a reassuringly familiar place to contemplate other worlds. Or to ponder the end of this one. Jodrell was the front line of the UK's nuclear defences before Fylingdales, and O'Brien points out that received wisdom for staff joining in the 80s was that there were still two Russian nukes trained on the site - and an American one, just in case it looked like the Russians had a chance of taking the site intact.

Snap out of Cold War nostalgia, and a closer look at the control room reveals an eclectic mix of cutting edge and seriously vintage kit. On one side some large flat screens were showing the dashboard for the eMerlin array. Everything was reassuringly green when we were there.

Across the room was a Compaq PC with some cannibalised HP CD drives which is used to monitor the onsite power generator. While the telescope sucks its juice from the national grid, if a power cut coincided with excessive wind at the site, the generator would kick in to allow the dish to be shifted into a position where it wasn't likely to take off into orbit itself.

Another rack shows the time according to both GPS and the station's own atomic clock. Splitting these gives you Jodrell time. (This after already adjusting our watch for both Earth and Venus time in the cafe.) In the next rack was a wood and brass hygrometer. While the same info is available on a screen in the control desk, sometimes scientists just seem to prefer paper and wood, says O'Brien.

Walk up close to the veteran control desk itself and you see a much more up to date array of flat panels controlling the movements of the telescope, though an old Vax terminal on the far right shows that this is an academic institution with heritage, and the urge to recycle. The Vaxes are near the end of their useful life for the site, said O'Brien, if only because of the scarcity of parts.

Talking of maintenance, a walk down the corridor - through numerous numberpad-sealed doors - took us to what looked like the ultimate garden shed. On one wall of the room is one of the most impressive arrays of wrenches we've seen outside of a KwikFit Centre. In the corner, you're treated to the sight of one of the scope's receivers hooked up to a life support system that uses helium to chill it down to the desired operating temperature of -260°C. Time almost slipped again here - the combination of the chemicals and the metronome's regular pumping could easily have transported you back to the Madchester of the 1990s.

A step further down the hall to the correlator would bring you sharply up to date. This is the two-rack machine that pulls together the feeds from the seven telescopes that make up the e-Merlin project, a task that keeps it ticking over at a brisk 1 peta ops per second. This would put it in the top 30 supercomputers in the world, but it isn't strictly a general purpose supercomputer.

Incidentally, if the pic on the right makes it look like it's in an enormous biscuit tin, that's 'cos it is. It's situated a few hundred feet from the main dish so to ensure it doesn't overwhelm the signals the dish is targeting, the correlator is enclosed in a box made of metal panels, with copper-sealed joints. Essentially it's a rather large, very noisy Faraday cage, throwing out around 1TB of data daily to be turned into astronomical images.

Feeding a beast like this requires huge amounts of data, drawn in from the optical network linking the stations that make up e-Merlin. The data used to be transmitted over radio links, but is now sucked into the site via a fibre-optic network, which includes 372.8 miles (600km) of pre-existing dark fibre and 55.9 miles (90km) of new fibre. This network allowed Jodrell to boost the sensitivity of the receivers by a factor of 20. This means it feeds the correlator at 210Gbps. Remember, that's a G. The UK public internet current tops out at around 1Tbps, meaning eMerlin alone is running at around a fifth of the UK's internet data. Put another way, O'Brien says on many projects the team can do in a day what used to take a year.

One further fact. The signals from the various telescopes have to be synced - this is done to an accuracy of 1-2 picoseconds.

If that sounds impressive, consider this. The site also includes two clusters - a pulsar research cluster running 1,440 CPU threads, and a modelling/ simulation cluster running 328 CPU threads.

With the site heading up the Square Kilometre Array project, the computing horsepower at Jodrell - and its sister site at Manchester - will be racking up its kit list as more physicists work their way up the M6 and settle onto the Cheshire Plain.

Sadly we didn't have time to check out the SKA building, or to rummage around in the older buildings that house old labs, hand-tooled Ferranti-era computers, and the site's hydrogen maser.

Even so, we were still 40 minutes late getting to the car park to meet the family. But at least we had the excuse of not knowing which time it was.

GPS
53.236819, -2.307330

Post code
SK11 9DL

Getting there
Around six miles from Jct 18 on the M6, just off the A535 between Holmes Chapel and Alderley Edge.

Entry
£7.50 for adults £5.50 for children. Family tickets £24 (although prices vary according to the time of day you visit).

Online resources
www.jodrellbank.net

Adastral Park
Suffolk

Dave Wilby

Inside Adastral: BT's Belgium-sized broadband boffinry base

Drive-by bragging rights

Adastral Park is BT's global research and development centre, one of the world's most pioneering centres of technology and telecommunications.

Like other visitors to the area, I've gazed at the Le Corbusier-inspired building and its iconic tower cube rising out of the surrounding flat Suffolk farmland. It announces its modernising mission to passengers staring out of the windows of cars hurtling along the A12 past Ipswich and on to the east coast.

The site has a rich history of military invention and technical achievement, and is now home to thousands of engineers not just working on the frontiers of boffinry but also turning new ideas into practical services.

BT calls Adastral Park "the home of UK broadband", and some insiders claim there's enough high-powered telecoms and computer kit on site to "run Belgium" – which is just a short hop across the North Sea. The park is a place that BT will open up as a science campus and a Suffolk ICT cluster if development plans are approved.

Yet the public knows relatively little about the site's rich history or what's there now. That's mostly because Adastral Park can only ever be a name to you for now – it's off-limits to most visitors. A glimpse from the A-road is the closest most will come. As part of *The Reg's Geek's Guide to Britain*, though, I was welcomed to the machine.

But let's go back to the beginning. The site has a long history of innovation. At the dawn of flight and aerial combat, a Royal Flying Corps aerodrome was established in 1916 in the village of Martlesham Heath. This became the Aeroplane and Armament Experimental Establishment, the main RAF airfield for the testing of prototype aircraft between 1924 and 1939. It witnessed the first flights of the Spitfire and the Hurricane.

In World War II it became an operational airbase and home to fighter aces such as Douglas Bader. In 1942 the airfield was taken over by the US Air Force and became the location of experimental military ballistics, electronics, rocketry, turbo engines and landing equipment before it was decommissioned in 1965.

Soon after the RAF moved out, the Post Office Research Laboratory relocated to Martlesham from Dollis Hill in London. The new telecommunications arm of the Post Office had blossomed since the end of the war, and Suffolk offered plenty of space for experimentation by physicists, chemists and engineers who had been instrumental in crucial projects such as the Colossus computer.

The open local countryside was ideal for testing radio-based communication systems. By 1975, the site was officially opened as BT Laboratories by the Queen, with the iconic tower building housing 1,700 BT Research staff.

Prestel, the world's first interactive commercial "videotex" data subscription service, was launched at Martlesham in 1979. In 1982, shortly after BT was privatised, its research site hosted Europe's first satellite transmission service, run by Eutelsat. BT Research demonstrated the world's first instant speech recognition and translation service in 1987 and as early as 1995 BT trialled a video-on-demand (VoD) service to thousands of customers in nearby Ipswich and Colchester using ADSL-over-copper to early set-top boxes.

From 1999 work to extend optical fibre transmission led to the launch of the UK's first commercial broadband internet service in June 2002, turning what had long been an academic technology into an engineering reality that British organisations, businesses and consumers could use.

Today, the renamed Adastral Park is BT's global innovation and development centre, an engineering HQ that takes top-flight technology and works out how to deploy and operate it in the real world.

It is a modern science park with more than 43 companies on site including some of the biggest names in IT: from Fujitsu and Ericsson to Samsung and Cisco. The site is also one of two worldwide Network Management Centres for BT Group, providing a 24-hour "follow-the-sun" service - the other being in El Segundo, California.

Welcome to Adastral Park, the "home" of UK broadband
Photo: Dave Wilby

It's also home to 4,000 IT professionals, 3,700 working on research, design, operations and consultancy.

As "the home of UK broadband", much of the work conducted on-site continues to explore the physical limits and practicalities of deploying a national standards-based super-fast broadband network at scale: how to actually get fibre to customers affordably and with the best possible performance.

Everything BT rolls out onto its network is tested to full operational standards across Adastral Park before it is deployed. In effect the park hosts a £500m scale model of BT's full global network, replicating every single piece of kit developed by BT and its interoperable vendors and suppliers – from cables and routers to digital multiplexers and telephone exchanges.

After negotiating a secure registration area, my introduction to Adastral Park was a landscaped campus surrounding that iconic Orion building and Pegasus tower complex. Many of these buildings are dedicated to research; its teams are trying to overcome communications challenges such as delivering fibre networks to telephone masts, monitoring conversations on social networks to improve services for customers, or designing smart communities and cities. Crucially, there is a real engineering function sitting behind the proof-of-concept systems.

But perhaps the most closely guarded area of Adastral Park that I was guided around is known as the "Four Acre Site" - a playground for physically testing and extending its new products, technologies, concepts and industry standards so that they are ready and optimised for deployment to real-world customers. One senior manager told me that Adastral Park nurtures one of the largest test and reference models in the world – "enough equipment on one site to run Belgium", as he put it.

Most of the work I was shown by BT's head engineers revolved around super-fast broadband and accelerating that last mile to homes and businesses. Technology is literally being tested in the field here, with new street-side junction boxes for fibre-to-the-cabinet and fibre-to-the premises projects sitting alongside weathering tests for long fibre runs.

I was shown the very latest designs in fibre cabling, blown using smart air compressors to blast the micro-textured fibre coating. This hands-on research in a Suffolk field is critical to BT delivering on its promise to deliver fibre broadband to two-thirds of the UK population by 2014 and 95 per cent of the UK by the end of 2017'. Just like me, staff from vendors and suppliers visit the site to gain confidence in how solutions would operate and adapt in real applications.

Back inside, Adastral Park's modestly titled Innovation Showcase puts into context the technologies on which BT and its partners are working. It can be a nebulous thing, discussing and selling an infrastructure or a service, so this facility lets BT show leading vendors how the physical products actually work.

Like an industry technology scout, I was able to play around with transparent and eyeball-tracking adverts, and footfall and movement analysis in mocked-up shops. Super-high-definition displays are placed in living room sets; other rooms are dressed for demonstrating technology in healthcare, hospitality, government, banking and pretty much any other market where there's a commercial interest. Whether it's integrating telecare into a patient's home entertainment system, or making product information available through augmented reality glasses, there's a showcase on tap.

Education is also a major part of BT's work at Adastral Park, and it aims to foster practical ICT, business studies and project management skills for future careers in the communications and IT sector. The company is a major employer in the area, so it is in its interests to make sure the right skills are coming through the education system and that a career in engineering and technology is attractive and accessible. In 2012 Adastral Park recruited around 70 graduates and 30 apprentices from nearby colleges and universities.

Members of an enthusiastic BT Education team told me they want children to be creators of technology again, not just users. They believe that while schools help children use software and devices, the youngsters are not encouraged to think about designing and developing products and technologies. The team now has a full licence to invest BT's cash in helping young Brits discover their creative spark and gain a passion for tech. I was able to have a quick play with some of the robotics challenges and interactive Lego projects being taught; in 2012 more than 4,300 young people from 70 schools and universities benefited from BT's education outreach programme in Suffolk.

BT is now working on plans to create 2,000 new jobs and provision for up to 2,000 homes by 2025, by opening up areas of Adastral Park as a science campus. The idea is to create a Suffolk research centre - a regenerated research and development facility that encourages the growth of an ICT cluster in Suffolk. The scheme is still dependent on support in the county for the development.

As I mentioned, Adastral Park is not generally open to the public, although it does welcome more than 60,000 invited visitors each year. The most you can hope for today is a drive by, pointing out to your fellow car passengers that strange rectangle and cube tower seemingly frozen mid-rotation. But it's worth the fleeting eyeful you'll get and the chance to explain what lies behind this most modern of facilities.

That means you can squeeze in a drive-by en-route to other destinations and attractions. Adastral Park is within a short drive of a number of historic East Anglian towns including Ipswich and Woodbridge. You can take the family to clamber on a castle at Colchesteror in Framlinghamget lost in the forests at Rendlesham or Thetford, take in the beach and brewery at Southwold, or grab a slice of culture at Aldeburgh or Snape Maltings, where a Santa lands via a Thames Barge every Christmas.

Refreshment is close by, too. Just out of sight of Adastral Park, yet signposted all the way, is The Maybush pub at Waldringfield on the banks of River Deben. It's a very friendly place to grab a great pint and some decent grub while watching the boats and wildlife float by. Slightly further afield but also on the Deben, is the historical town of Woodbridge, with a broad choice of inns and eateries, such as the 16th century pub Ye Olde Bell & Steelyard, or The Waterfront Café in the ancient tide mill.

If you're looking for accommodation near Adastral Park, there are some great inns in Woodbridge such as The Crown, or the luxury four-star Tudor hotel set Seckford Hall. But if you've made the trip this far east, then why not go the whole hog, head to the coast, and get yourself a guesthouse, hotel or holiday cottage in a cosy seaside hideout in Southwold, Dunwich, Walberswick or Aldeburgh?

GPS
52.058032,1.2795

Post code
IP5 3RE

Getting there
By car: A14 from the Midlands and North until you have crossed the Orwell Bridge, then the A12 north to the turning for the park at Martlesham Heath. From London or the south, take the M25 and then A12, crossing the bridge on the A14, before re-joining the A12. Train to Ipswich, and shuttle from bus station.

Entry
Not open to the public.

Online resources
ww.atadastral.co.uk

LEO – the Lyons Electronic Office
London

Gavin Clarke

GEEK'S
GUIDE
TO BRITAIN

Blighty's revolutionary Cold War teashop computer - and Nigella Lawson

Nuclear missile with your sponge finger, sir?

The Victorian offices were bulldozed long ago for a stack of flats and mirrored offices, and there's not a single indication as to the significance of this site - or what happened here.

This isn't the scene of a lost battle, and the bones of a missing Plantagenet king do not slumber beneath the car park serving the offices.

No 66 Hammersmith Road in London is the scene of a revolution - a revolution in computing that changed how business operated; a revolution during which Britain, briefly, led the technology pack.

That's because this site was once home to the LEO - the Lyons Electronic Office, the subject of a permanent display at the Science Museum, which opened in September 2014. You may already have heard of LEO, described as the world's first business computer. It's a shorthand description, though, that makes the LEO sound about as fascinating and forgettable as a beige box running DOS.

But LEO wasn't a personal computer running Lotus 1-2-3: it was a hulk, a room-sized colossus built by J Lyons and Co to organise its bakery business; it ran its first program in 1951. The computer was jumped on by manufacturers, City stockbrokers, nationalised industries and even apple growers who immediately recognised the machine's potential to save them time and money in the march to efficiency.

This was also the early Cold War era, and the LEO came to the attention of the military industrial complex. The business brain was quickly deployed to the front lines on both sides of the Iron Curtain. Although the LEO was used to build Britain's nuclear deterrent against the communists' warheads (the doomed Blue Streak missile project that ultimately never actually worked) the machine was also shipped to the very regimes with which the US and Great Britain were at loggerheads.

War is hell, battle-hardened American Civil-War General William Sherman observed, but business is also business. The communists also had plenty of data to crunch, but no computers. It was, therefore, in the land of the people's commissars that Britain outsold the blue shirts of New York-headquartered IBM; LEOs popped up in the Soviet Union and Soviet-controlled satellite states including Czechoslovakia.

The LEO's makers were pioneers in software development and testing, and they refined the processes needed to run very large and complex computing jobs. Later revisions of the machine could share processor time across multiple scheduled work, known as multitasking these days, utilising spare capacity to run different jobs; it was a feature the machine's designers eventually turned into a business. The team also engaged in business process engineering and use of real-time analysis before these entered the lingua bizza of today.

Also, the world's first woman business programmer worked on the LEO.

Yet, the computer wasn't the work of well-funded government engineers or university boffins, as was the fashion for other massive number-crunchers of the Atomic Era. The LEO was commissioned by one of the biggest catering and food manufacturers in the world, a company famed for biscuits, ice creams and teashops, serving that most noble of beverages - the cuppa.

And that business, J Lyons and Co, also happens to have given us Nigella Lawson. The journalist and food writer is the great-granddaughter of Lyons' managing director Alfred Salmon and a great-great-granddaughter of one of Lyons' founding members Barnett Salmon.

So, how did it come to pass that a biccie company, created in 1887, put Britain on the front line of business computing? The firm was headquartered in a two-acre manufacturing and administration operation called Cadby Hall; the main office number was 66 Hammersmith Road. From the start, Lyons was on the hunt for new ideas to improve its operations and stay in front of the competition.

The LEO's roots lay with the company's brilliant hiring of Cambridge maths whiz John Simmons nearly 20 years before the bulky computer actually ran its first job in 1951. Simmons' job was to find ways of keeping Lyons at the forefront of new ideas, so he set up a systems research office in 1932 staffed by engineers, business people and fellow mathematicians.

In 1946, Simmons sent Lyons managers Oliver Standinford and Raymond Thompson to the US on a fact-finding mission to report back on technology developed during the war, particularly in electronics. The pair met Herman Goldstine - one of the creators of the 30-ton ENIAC, the first electronic general-purpose computer. The ENIAC was a vast system announced in 1946 and built by the US military to calculate missile trajectories. In a paper to the Lyons board, Thompson called computers the key to office efficiency and reckoned Lyons could build a computer for £100,000 and cut annual office expenses by £50,000.

LEO 1 – the world's first commercial computer
Photo: Leo Computers Society

Thompson had been completely unaware of Maurice Wilkes' work on the early British calculator EDSAC at the University of Cambridge, but soon learned of the project. Lyons donated £3,000 to help Wilkes finish the EDSAC and to influence the design, and Lyons also put a man on the team to learn about the circuitry. The company hired a Cambridge graduate named John Pinkerton as an electronic engineer; Pinkerton became the LEO's engineering manager.

These were truly early days of computer manufacture: there were no assembly-line robots, silicon chip fabs and injection-mould plastics specialists forming a supply chain to build the LEO. Instead it was carpenters, plumbers, sheet-metal workers and engineers working on thermionic valves, switches, wires, ducting, resistors and power supplies. The LEO was built at a factory on Minerva Road in Acton, West London, and moved in crates to Cadby Hall, where it was assembled.

The LEO was more or less the EDSAC: it sported 3,000 electronic valves, 32 storage tanks that held 32 numbers of 17 binary digits, and executed 650 instructions per second.

Compare that to today's computing power: take an ARM Cortex-A8 processor core used in Apple's A4 system-on-a-chip on the iPad. That runs 2,000 million instructions per second (Dhrystone MIPS) at 1.0 GHz. Too fancy? Want more of a workhorse comparison? Try the Intel Core i7 875K that executes 92,100 DMIPS at 2.93 GHz. The iPad also packs 16GB or 32GB of memory. The 80286, the Intel chip that helped ignite the PC revolution of the 1980s, although heavily out-gunned today, was capable of 2.66 DMIPS at 12.5 MHz and of addressing 16MB of RAM.

Data was fed into the EDSAC on teleprinter paper tape via an electromechanical tape reader that, by 1950, was updated to a photoelectric reader. The output was initially through a teleprinter upgraded to a paper tape punch in 1951. For the LEO, its designers hoped to use magnetic tape for memory storage but it never worked properly so mercury ultrasonic delay lines – acoustic signals travelling through the fluid to be later turned back into electronic signals - were used instead. These were capable of holding just over 1,000 combinations of characters. The operating system consisted of 41 data words of read-only memory.

Where the LEO differed from the EDSAC was in the modifications made by Lyons to make it business-ready. Input and output channels were added so LEO could read and write simultaneously, allowing it to multitask better, whereas EDSAC had a single channel for input and output. Lyons extended the basic operating system using macros written by an inexperienced team of computer programmers, who wrote special instructions for things such as addition, subtraction and currency conversion.

Every macro was written on a piece of paper, checked by another person, and overseen by the man who ascended to manager of the Lyons Systems Research Office David Caminer, a veteran of the Second World War who lost a leg in North Africa who later became a director of LEO Computers. The programmers had varied backgrounds; Mary Coombs, the world's first business computer programmer, was a French graduate, while another coder called Frank Land was a grad from the London School of Economics (LSE).

To work on the LEO, a developer had to pass various tests to prove they had the crucial skill of clear, logical thought. Land, who had worked in the Lyons statistics office, programmed the new apps; by 1967 he was the chief consultant responsible for the LEO systems teams across Britain.

Speaking to *The Register*, Land recalled that it was Caminer who drove the Lyons LEO team hard. Land said Caminer set the standard: "He, in a sense, invented software engineering of business processes – he was meticulous, he was a tyrant, but instilled standards in us that made things work. He made you write the documentation and if he didn't like it, he flung it at you."

The big date celebrated in the LEO's history is 5 September 1951 when the first program was run - an application known as Bakery Valuations. The first LEO calculated the profits and costs of running its ovens, from the fuel needed to make the food to the ingredients, staff wages and distribution to the shops, cafes and restaurants. These calculations had been performed by Lyons' army of 5,000 accountants armed with calculating machines but the LEO broke the job down into small units, so if there was a problem it could be restarted without losing track of the data. The program went from being performed once a week to being executed in just a couple of hours.

It's this date that was celebrated in 2011 as the 60th anniversary of the LEO business computer. But the machine didn't actually become operational until 24 December, 1953. That was when the Lyons bosses felt the LEO was reliable enough to trust it to run the business. Between 1951 and 1953, Land's team had to find bugs in the computer's apps, and they developed procedures to follow should the LEO break down mid-job. It was Pinkerton who oversaw the work getting the LEO running properly and developing safety procedures.

"We developed ways to test the computer and ensure it worked and on how to overcome problems, and on the system side how to divide jobs, so if there was a breakdown it could be started without wasting what had been done," Land told *The Reg*. "We couldn't get anything on the computer until it had been checked by second programmer - the most pressing thing was computer time."

As with computers in business today, Lyons quickly found lots of different and probably unexpected uses for the LEO beyond cup-cake counting. The payroll for 10,000 staff went on the second LEO machine, LEO II, in February 1954. In October that year, data from Lyons' network of more than 200 teashops went into the LEO to manage the tea-time treats empire in real-time, or as close as possible to that.

Lyons was famed for its network of 250 teashops in Blighty - these were meticulously designed and staffed by waitresses in smart black uniforms; you were never far from a Lyons teashop in town. It was said there was a Lyons teashop every 100 yards in the centre of London, with its cafes scattered around Piccadilly, Kings Cross and other upmarket surroundings.

Problem was, there wasn't much margin in a cup of tea – a cuppa cost about two shillings and two pennies or less than two quid today, while the shops slapped on plenty of costs: food was cooked, frozen and delivered across the country from central bakeries to prime high-street locations each day. Also, the teashops had an 80 per cent annual staff turnover, making calculating the payroll a moving challenge. Lyons hit on the idea to make and ship to shops only what was needed based on anticipated next-day demand.

So, starting in October 1954, the manageress – and, yes, they were all women - of each teashop would call the Hammersmith HQ from a pay-phone near her shop at an allocated time to relay her shop's orders. She gave the shop's code – starting with "A" for Piccadilly – each item's code and the quantity, recording just the deviation from a standard order. Each order covered milk, tea, sandwiches, cakes and cooked meals. The LEO calculated production requirements, delivery schedules, invoices and management reports - all done overnight.

"This was as near a real-time system as you could get," Land told *The Reg*. "Thousands of individual pieces of data were coming in each day. By today's standards that was tiny but by the standards of then that was miraculous. One lived in an era of excitement because every day we were doing something new."

The nearest competition, ABC's Teashops owed by Canadian businessman and philanthropist Garfield Weston, used hole-punch machines to computerise its operations - a clunky technology rejected by Lyons because it lacked the flexibility to deal with the business changes taking place.

The LEO also calculated the blends of tea, and how to mix them to maintain a consistency of flavour given the quality of the local water – it was decades ahead of Starbucks, who today wants its coffee to taste exactly the same in

Leicester Square, London, as it does in Union Square, San Francisco. Each week Lyons received data on tea from auctions, gardeners, growers and from its own people.

"The LEO kept track of movements of tea in the warehouse and costs of tea for use in the blending process – this was done on a daily basis," Land said.

Other organisations got wind of the LEO thanks to Simmons rubbing shoulders with chiefs in his capacity as president and founder of the Association of Business Managers. The Meteorological Office ran climate calculations on the LEO in December 1951, payrolls from Ford UK, Tate & Lyle, Kodak and the British Army found their way onto the computer, and the beast was used by British Rail to calculate the distance between each and every railway station in the country, 5,000 stations. The LEO team had to write an algorithm to process that specific job. All these calculations were run when Lyons wasn't using the LEO.

It was in 1952 that the LEO joined the Cold War. Aerospace manufacturer De Havilland was building a medium-range ballistic missile called Blue Streak to hurl a nuclear warhead back at the Soviets. When Lyons wasn't working out the profits on cakes, De Havilland's men would show up at Hammersmith, rope off the area around the LEO to keep out regular employees and run ballistic calculations. "We couldn't see what was going on," Land recalled.

Blue Streak, riddled with political and logistical problems, was scrapped in 1960 and De Havilland ended up buying its own LEO machine. But Lyons got a sniff of the potential. In 1954 Lyons created LEO Computers with T R Thompson as managing director; the biz built LEO I's successors, the LEO II and LEO III. The LEO III replaced valves with germanium transistors, and mercury delay lines with ferrite-core memory, creating a much faster, cooler and more reliable machine that backed its data up onto magnetic tape. It was what Caminer called "a world-beating machine".

LEO Computers sold the electronic monsters and provided outsourced services – the bureau service - and it was Land's brother Ralph who opened the first LEO bureau, in Hartree House, Bayswater. It was Ralph Land, too, who took the LEO to the world, and particularly the communists, against American giant IBM at the height of the Cold War. Ralph, also an LSE graduate, said he joined Lyons because he'd seen his brother doing well on what he gamely described as "the computer side".

Ralph told *The Reg* of the moment the LEO's chief Thompson decided to punt the LEO to the communists: "Thompson told me: 'We are not doing business overseas, but we are selling the LEOs at home. We should develop the overseas business.' I spoke German, so it was decided I should take over the export business."

Thompson reckoned Eastern Europe was "the soft underbelly" of the continent ripe for exploitation because no one from the West was selling there due to restrictions in place during the Cold War. Ralph soon ran LEO Computers' Eastern European bureau with 80 employees. The first LEO III was sold to the Czech Ministry for Social Security and Czech Railways, doing clerical and scheduling. Ralph says he was outselling IBM, which had 250 workers in its central Eastern European head office in Vienna, Austria. Big Blue had just started to sell the first System 360 mainframes.

But Ralph had to tread carefully. The Cold War was in full swing, the US was gripped by McCarthyism, the Soviets had erected a great wall across Berlin, and Moscow and Washington were squaring off over missiles in Cuba. Laws controlled what could be sold to the USSR and its satellite states, similar to today's restrictions on sales of computer and engineering parts to Iran and North Korea. But the communists wanted LEOs and were prepared to use blackmail or bribery to get them.

"We had to be extremely careful that our people weren't got at and that we worked within the limits of the embargo," Ralph told us. "That let us sell LEO IIIs, although I had to go to the US State department to argue the case for selling the computers; but we built up a pretty subsidiary business - in a sense I always argued we had control over their economies. If their ministries relied on our computers and they did anything war-like, we could stop selling spare part."

Ralph claimed LEO Computers was a more patient and flexible business than IBM. For example, it took two years and 19 different signatures, up to and including the Prime Minister, to straddle the Iron Curtain and sell a computer to the Soviets.

The communists, meanwhile, also lacked the hard currency needed to pay for the LEO IIIs. Ralph's answer was to institutionalise a system of bartering: the company accepted ball bearings from Romania and hanging baskets from Bulgaria as payment for machines, which the firm swiftly sold on.

When it came to flogging the LEO to Czechoslovakia, Ralph's team financed a movie made by a Prague-based film studio; once the flick was completed and shown, it earned foreign currency and LEO Computers pocketed the proceeds as payment for the computer.

"On the basis of this, sufficient funds were made available for the municipality to acquire and pay for the computer," Ralph said. At his operation's peak, he had nine people bartering.

"The trick in the barter trade is to find the customer who wanted it, so we never saw the stuff," Ralph said.

"We beat IBM, I think, because we were more flexible in dealing with the Eastern Europeans and USSR rather than the more ideological approach of the Americans," he added. "I said if we were going to counter-trade, let's do it properly – let's set up a counter-trade bureau."

IBM's Vienna office was downgraded from a regional HQ to a country office in 2008, but the building is still a grand affair; a crisp, rectangle of blue-green glass on 95 Donaustraße. The office's status changed as IBM won the computing war. Vienna is now a business analytics centre and software lab specialising in the banking and financial sector. It operates as a cog within a cog of the Big Blue machine - part of the $7.9bn software business that forms part of IBM's global $104.5bn revenue. IBM doesn't say how many employees IBM Vienna has these days, but the tech giant has just under half-a-million workers globally.

Inside the LEO's delay line battery coffins
Photo: Leo Computers Society

On the other end of the scale is 66 Hammersmith Road. What hits you first is the space: Lyons' two-acre complex fell to the wrecking ball years ago and the area was massively opened up by the developer: on the site of No 66 is a nicotine-brown mirrored building named The Kensington Centre, with offices to let, fringed by shrubs, a small car park and a throbbing main road, the A315. The Kensington Centre is today home to various companies while behind it sits a layered complex of flats.

Ralph's adventure in Eastern Europe was an insufficient counterweight to IBM's global scale. The people running LEO Computers focused too much on positioning and not enough on technology. The biz merged with the computer interests of English Electric in 1963 to form English Electric LEO, which became English Electric Leo Marconi (EELM) and finally, in 1968, ICL in a deal brokered by firebrand Labour MP Tony Benn, who was Harold Wilson's Minister of Technology.

Benn wanted to create a British computer industry to compete with IBM, so had arranged the forced marriage that created ICL. This was the era of nationalisation, when political orthodoxy held that choice and competition were best served by having a single service provider in each sector, from railways to airlines, the telephone to fuel – British Rail, British Airways, British Telecom and British Gas.

The best ICL could achieve was Europe's fourth largest IT company and, in 1990, Fujitsu took an 80 per cent stake. Talk of a spin-out remained just talk, and Fujitsu finally shot the ICL brand in the head in 2001.

Lyons breathed its last in the decade before. The teashop titan had loaded up on debt to fund a round of massive expansions that bloated it during the 1970s. Lyons bought into ice creams and booze with Baskin Robbins and Pedro Domecq of Spain among others, in addition to running a network of 44 hotels. Lyons also doubled down on baking and shipping foods, investing in new regional bakeries.

The company closed teashop after teashop, but this alone wasn't enough and in 1978 it was bought by Allied Breweries to become Allied Lyons. But these were grim economic times, and a struggling Lyons was finally broken up in the 1980s during the reign of the Conservative Party and Blighty's Chancellor Nigel Lawson, father of the aforementioned Nigella. Lyons' ice cream and lolly biz became Lyons Maid and was sold to Nestlé; Lyons Cakes was sold to the firm that owns Mr Kipling and Lyons Biscuits was sold in 1994, ending up with Burton's Foods.

Nobody can say whether the LEO lived up to Thompson's promise to cut expenses or whether it helped Lyons become efficient - I asked Frank and Ralph, and they reckon nobody really knew. Certainly, Lyons hadn't absorbed Thompson's message of efficiency through computerisation, and the company's failings were the result of flawed human decision-making and business models.

At best, the LEO extended Lyons' life as post-war labour costs shot up thanks to a growing demand for semi-skilled and clerical staff - the kind of employees the LEO was replacing. But the computer alone was unable to compensate for the humans who made bad business decisions or who failed to embrace the practices in business computing and business process engineering they'd begun.

"Lyons' management were extremely innovative... but were unprepared to change the basic model of the teashop operation," Ralph said.

Where the LEO succeeded was in tapping a demand. Organisations had always amassed sales and other business data, but using it in a way to cut costs while delivering what the customer wanted and doing so at low price? That was the rub. The LEO helped businesses and governments realise this.

Had Lyons taken its passion for new ideas to its fullest extent and bet on computers rather than cakes, then LEO Computers might still be here and a peer to IBM. But food was its trade, and Lyons was flogged into the ground while the British government and various LEO management teams spent too long organising and not enough time executing.

"The LEO story is where, for a little slice of time, this country led the computer industry," Ralph said. "We ultimately failed because not enough money was put into it and we were outsold by the volume of effort our rivals could put in rather than the quality of the product.

"Where we did outsell them, that was due to our approach in a different environment. We had a much more flexible approach and we could outsell them in Eastern Europe."

Today, you can view the site of 66 Hammersmith Road from the comfort of a pub and several eateries opposite. There's the Albion that specialises in pizzas; a few doors down, Café Paradiso that serves tea, coffee and sandwiches; and there's a Thai place called Kanna. Carry on and you soon hit the shops and gastro-pubs of Hammersmith. Go in the opposite direction and you reach the Mirabell Cucina for Mediterranean food and in a few minutes you'll be at Olympia, home of the conference venue and scene to tech events.

Next time you are shopping in Hammersmith or itching to get away from that tech confab at Olympia, take a short walk along Hammersmith Road. Grab a bite to eat – better still, a cuppa - and, remember and reflect: it was on this spot, amidst the flour and leaves of tea, that Blighty stumbled into a revolution.

GPS
51.494784,-0.212688

Post code
W14 8UD

Getting there
Nearest tube: Barons Court, Piccadilly Line and District Line; West Kensington, District Line.

Entry
N/A

Online resources
LEO: First Business Computer, by Peter Bird
www.leo-computers.org.uk
www.kzwp.com/lyons

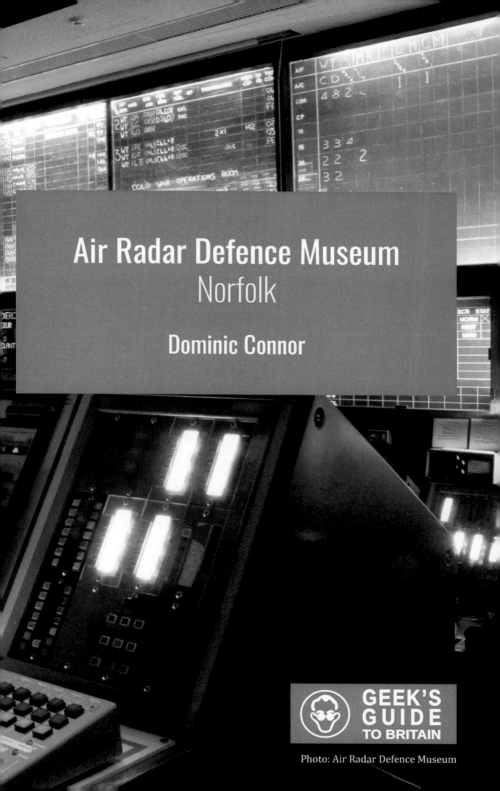

Air Radar Defence Museum
Norfolk

Dominic Connor

GEEK'S GUIDE TO BRITAIN

Reg man bested in geek-to-geek combat - in World War III nerve centre

Dom Connor and the cool Cold Warriors

During the Cold War, Neatishead in Norfolk was theoretically the worst place in the UK to live: the nearby RAF base would be target Number One if the Russians nuked us.

This was brought home to me in a guided tour by a retired officer, whose old job was to run Blighty's air defence. Standing in the 1980s-era Cold War control room it was genuinely moving to hear how, in drills for World War III, the countdown clock would start ticking down to the time when Soviet missiles would detonate over the UK and the order would come for everything that could fly to take off and try to ride out the storm.

This wasn't a show put on for a visiting journo; what has become the Air Defence Radar Museum (ADRM) is run by the people who really did this stuff when it was an operational centre of the nation's air defence.

When the RAF left Neatishead and decommissioned the site in 2006, the top brass just turned out the lights and left. Now, however, you can tour something that was once about the most secret place in Britain, with the added positive that you can sit down and touch the actual equipment that once (hopefully) showed what the enemy was up to and could dispatch missiles and aircraft in our defence.

While strolling around the museum, I'd become a little delocalised but I was pretty sure we hadn't gone underground to a nuclear bunker. There was a bunker, but someone broke it; an irked airman had started a fire in 1966 and, being underground where fire fighting is not fun, it was wrecked. The base's firemen were unable to extinguish the blaze, and their civvy colleagues were summoned. Three perished and the man responsible got jail time.

RAF Neatishead, about 11 miles from Norwich center, was established by the RAF in 1941 as the site for a brand-new air defence station to direct fighters.

The first, secret radar system was installed in September that year and played a crucial role in getting the RAF's birds up against Luftwaffe day and night time attacks on military and industrial targets across Norfolk, including Norwich.

Neatishead occupies 25 acres and 17 buildings that included radar tower and underground operations block, and that went up for sale in July 2015 valued at £2.5m. The museum itself is housed in the old 1942 operations block.

Radar's finest hour was during the Second World War when RAF Neatishead operated mobile and static units against the Jerries. The base had one of the first operational 1938 Chain Home Radar systems and a Battle of Britain ops room with the original Biggin Hill scoreboard.

The 1942 room covers the night Blitz and there is a mockup of the complex process of tracking enemy bombers and ensuring that harm came to them. As in the Cold War room, there are proper experts on this stuff to explain it all and very realistic it is too, except that - apparently - all that stood between the Nazis and our green and pleasant land was a bunch of mannequins sporting dodgy hairdos.

There is a tracking demo, where you get to understand just how tough it was to bring together up and down with left to right scans in three dimensions without a computer to do the heavy lifting, at a time when the blips were coming to kill you.

As well as all that, there's technical gear from RAF Fylingdales including a bit of one of the infamous radar golfball shields. Actually, Neatishead has acquired lots of bits over the years.

These include beautifully intricate electronic valves, the cockpit of a Jaguar ground-attack craft, an (allegedly) disarmed Bristol Bloodhound surface-to-air missile, original magnetrons, helmets, and what is frankly an apparently random selection of aerospace relics, mostly well-labelled. My kids were particularly impressed by the guy showing in real-time the maelstrom that is the air traffic over the UK and in particular how a chunk of it is stacked over our house.

Here's the big question: will you enjoy the museum?

Not if you just turn up, no. Because it's run by enthusiasts it is not open every day so you must check the website first. I'm a serious geek and it's not unknown when I wander round museums for me to "acquire" other visitors and lead them round explaining (sometimes even correctly) the exhibits rather better than the real staff.

But that didn't happen here. I was utterly outclassed by more experts than you are ever likely to meet at the Science Museum. You will learn interesting stuff, if you like the history of tech and war. The ADRM is about technology for and by the people who made the damned stuff work.

Bloodhound poised: missile at the Air Radar Defence Museum
Photo: Air Radar Defence Museum

The optional tour is about 90 minutes and I'd say there's at least an extra half hour's fun to be had talking to the staff about the exhibits. Unless you know or care more about radar than me, then it's not rational to go solo: you will need this stuff explained to you.

I personally despise the way so many museums have leased their catering to outfits who offer overpriced pseudo-Mediterranean fare. The ADRM does sandwiches, optionally toasted, soup and other simple grub. It's not bad value, given that the only other food for miles requires you to hunt it down.

There is, of course, a small gift shop that won't rip you off with its stock of badges, books and so on. Unlike a depressingly growing set of museums (I shall not name the one in which I was ordered to delete a photo of my son sitting in a chair) this place doesn't indulge in copyright fascism. You can take all the photos you want.

My eight- and 11-year-old boys really enjoyed it: they're a bit more geeky than the average lad, but you're a *Reg* reader, so I guess yours may be the same. That said, eight is likely to be the lowest age able to hold their attention for the full stay.

I have never visited a museum where my kids got the chance to press so many buttons and that alone justified it for them. My Reassuringly Expensive Lawyer™ wife got a lot out of it as well, but watching me be out-geeked was the highlight for her. Apparently.

GPS
52.713198N, 1.471649E

Post code
NR12 8YB

Getting there
A149 from Great Yarmouth or A1151 from Norwich, then A1062 to just outside Horning

Entry
£8 for adults, £7 for concessions and £5 for 7-18-year-olds, under 7 free, family tickets (two adults and up to three children) £20

Online resources
www.radarmuseum.co.uk

BT Tower
London

Joe Fay

Photo: Fenke Fros

BT Tower is just a relic? Wrong. It relays 18,000 hours of telly daily

The Reg goes inside and up Blighty's telecoms spire

The Post Office Tower in London, adorned with microwave dishes and resembling a gigantic *Star Trek* gadget, symbolised the UK's white heat for technology in the 1960s.

In an era of the transistor radio as fashion accessory, the space race, and the arrival of Doctor Who, this alien cylinder of glass and metal stood proud.

It was also designed to operate through the white heat of a nuclear apocalypse. It's got a war room underneath, but the shutters on that underground bunker were brought down after a half-arsed bomb attack on the revolving restaurant at the top of the tower in 1971.

The explosion was attributed to the Provisional IRA, but it was actually conceived and carried out by an otherwise barely coherent bunch of anarchists. The structure was closed to the general public a decade later.

In most people's minds, however, the building's most terrifying enemy was a gigantic fluffy white pussycat that struck in 1972 on *The Goodies*.

Moving on to the present day, the tower is arguably still the most important communications nerve centre in the UK, but this has little to do with its original purpose.

It started life as The Post Office Tower: a radio mast designed as a hub for a national microwave network that was seen as the future of telecoms.

It was officially opened in 1965, four years after construction started.

According to a wonderful 1970 brochure given to us by BT, the spire - later renamed the BT Tower - was expected to provide four microwave paths, carrying "150,000 simultaneous telephone conversations or 100 both-way television channels".

This could be increased with the addition of more aerials - if such a preposterous amount of communications capacity was ever needed.

So when Eric Bedford and G. R. Yeats of the Ministry of Public Building and Works began designing the building, the requirements were, well, just make something very tall. OK, specifically, something so tall we can hang radio masts and dishes on it to give 360-degree coverage - and it must sway no more than 10 inches even in the face of 95mph winds.

So, that'll be a tall tower that is round and slim.

The tower itself is 581ft (177m) high, plus a 12m nest of antennas at the top. Rising up from the crucially important Museum Exchange just north of Oxford Street, this was more than enough to peer northwards over the Chilterns.

It was the tallest thing in London until the 600ft (183m) Tower 42 (the Natwest Tower to the rest of us) opened in 1980. The telecoms tower is currently the 10th highest structure in the capital, although the Greater London Authority's incontinent planning policy will push it further down the list over the coming years.

Once London's tallest structure BT Tower now ranks 10th.
Photo: Fenke Fros

However, while many of us might find the likes of Canary Wharf and The Shard oppressive, the Post Office Tower quickly wormed its way into our affections. I think this is in part because it was never a high citadel of plutocrats looking down on us while shuffling tax-free money around the world. It doesn't glower or aggressively shoulder its way onto the skyline with all the other well-lit concrete and glass.

It's just there, slenderly popping up whenever you turn a corner in the West End, or crest the top of the North Downs. And it was, after all, the Post Office Tower, in its own way a community communications resource, that "we" nominally owned, had brief access to, and had certainly paid for.

Four ship engine's power the tower in the event of outage.
Photo: Fenke Fros

The best way to appreciate how slim the tower is, is to get underneath. Not just on the street, but right underneath all 13,000 tons of it. So that's what we did a couple of weeks ago, taking a tour under and through the tower courtesy of BT.

The public areas of the tower have had a number of facelifts over the years - partly in response to security concerns, partly to reflect the transition from GPO to British Telecommunications. to BT, as the UK incumbent telco was spun out of state control.

Down in the bowels, things are reassuringly unchanged. To get there, we walked through a room of System X kit, dropped down to the "sub-basement", before crossing a corridor with a mysterious water tank, and old filing cabinets spanning multiple decades. We then had to shimmy up a ladder to get into the chamber under the shaft itself.

The core concrete shaft is just 34.4ft (10.5m) in diameter, and 2ft (0.61m) thick at its widest point. It slims down to just 6.05m in diameter, with walls just 0.98ft (0.3m) thick. The tower's core rests on a 21ft (6.5m) high concrete pyramid, which itself rests on a 90ft (27.5m) square, 2.95ft (0.9m) thick concrete raft. The pyramid, according to that wonderful 1970 vintage brochure BT gave us, actually protrudes one foot above ground level.

Some say the raft floats on a "bed of oil", but we've not been able to get that confirmed. BT's bumf simply refers to the foundations being dug into London's distinct "blue clay" - which at least matches the telco's corporate colour scheme.

To describe this construction as small is, obviously, overstating it, but to get an idea of just how compact the shaft is, consider the size of the light fittings or the Henry vacuum cleaner in our photos, or simply the curve of the base of the tower.

And at the base, there's some ancient graffiti and some cleaning equipment. In the gully around the bottom of the pyramid there's some water that's seeped in, along with an ancient tin bucket - just in case. This scene could be from any time in the last 50 years, with only the odd pair of discarded trainers and the grinning Henry giving much in the way of time cues.

It's NOT the bottom of the world's tallest rubbish chute... but it is under the pyramid.

Those wooden struts aren't actually holding up the tower, you'll be reassured to know, but access covers just below ground level.

"We haven't seen any rats, but we think we've seen the footprints in the dust on the cables," said our guide, facilities engineer Mark Polley. "So wash your hands when you head up to the restaurant."

There are other, mysterious chambers under the pyramid. Somewhere down there is the "war room", apparently complete with bunk beds and chemical toilets. No mention of tinned foods. Perhaps that would have been sent down from the Billy Butlin-operated restaurant at the top.

Polley reckoned "war room" was a slightly euphemistic title. The tower was designed to withstand a nuclear blast a mile away, but in the event of hostilities breaking out, it's difficult to believe that London would have been subject to just one blast, or that the incoming missile would've been that accurate. More likely, in his opinion, it was to deal with civil disorder - the original specification included a central locking system that the front desk guards would have hit in the event of the building coming under attack; "strikes", as Polley put it.

Somewhere down there are four ship engines as well, which can power the tower in the event of an outage - again, just in case of strikes. That machinery was also off limits the day we visited.

The tower itself is only 20m in diameter at its widest, and the much more slender core carries the two lifts and ducts for power, telecoms and other utilities. The original lifts were the fastest in Europe, whisking diners and engineers to the top at a cracking 1,299ft (365.76m) a minute. Sadly, they were decommissioned some time ago. Happily the new lifts are a nifty 1,400ft (426.72m) per minute, getting you from the underground level to the top in under 30 seconds - or put another way, just long enough to get your camera out and get a snap of the digital counter whizzing round.

Dave Lemm, our lift operator, has been on the job for 25 years, which was the longest anyone we met there had been at the tower... but not by much. For such a narrow building, people don't seem to want to leave.

That blue sheeting in the pics is because the lifts were being used to shift gear up to the restaurant for an event the day we visited. Operating BT Tower's lifts is just as glamorous a job as it was back in the 1960s. While the public hasn't been able to visit since the turn of the 1980s, BT hosts 600 events a year at the tower, many of them linked to its charity operations. In fact, *El Reg* has paid a visit once before, to a BT/Football Association event that included luminaries such as ex-Arsenal player Martin Keown and that bloke who played *East Ender* hard man Phil Mitchell.

This time we had it to ourselves, bar our guides and the catering staff getting ready for that evening's event. Remember we said the restaurant floor was 20m in diameter? If this sounds cosy, consider that includes the core of the building. The actual rotating floor width is 3.35m. If you were having a Martini up here back in the day, you really were in exclusive company. The 1970 brochure said you could balance a penny on the floor as it revolved, three times an hour, and it would not topple (the coin, not the tower). It really is that smooth in our experience. Neither a soap star nor a footballer showed the slightest wobble on our previous visit. There is an emergency stop button and we took a picture:

An aside: we'd never really considered how the windows were cleaned. Growing up in 1970s London, one was accustomed to grime (again, thank the strikes). Happily tower manager Karen Ahern - 19 years at the steel spire - explained the system to us. There are two poles outside the window, down which a one-man basket is lowered. Someone hits a button, the restaurant rotates, and the window cleaner in the bucket gets busy with a squeegee.

Yes, it does seem a bit of a waste of a view. And yes, those views are magnificent. It was a fine spring day when we visited, with just enough cloud cover to look picturesque without obscuring the view to the North Downs, Chilterns, or your chosen home county's pastures.

The comms giant insists those regular rumours of the revolving restaurant reopening are nothing to do with it - with 600 events a year in the tower, it's not like it's letting the space go unused. And while it's a shame more people can't enjoy the view, BT can at least now direct people to The Shard. An illustrative point here: in the 1960s, it cost four shillings to go up the tower (£3.28 in today's money). A trip up The Shard costs £25.95 for an adult, or £19.95 for a child. There were plenty of spaces available at short notice last time we looked...

If you did take a trip up The Shard, and looked across the river at the BT Tower, you'd notice how bare the old equipment gantries look, since the last dish was taken down in 2011.

If you've been paying attention you've probably been thinking, "hang on, so the restaurant's revolving, but no one can go up there these days, and the microwaves up there will be for the ready meals. What's it all for, then?"

Well, there's still good old-fashioned telecoms kit in there working away. This network is gradually being broken down, though Ahern said some of the line cards can't be disconnected as the labels have wilted away over the years, and they're wary of cutting someone off unexpectedly. Still, as the pics show, work carries on apace.

But archaeological telecoms apart, the tower - or at least the tower site - is still gainfully employed in the communications business, albeit almost by accident, as Jonathan Wing, BT Media and Broadcast's global sales director tells it.

The story begins (of course) back in the 1960s. Even as London's elite were getting used to the novelty of being able to talk to Southampton or Birmingham via microwave, or sip a Chivas Regal at the top of a building built to withstand a nuclear blast, communications satellites were starting to girdle the globe at a much higher altitude, while somewhere "down there" optical fibre was on the cusp of becoming a reliable telecoms medium.

Meanwhile, outside, at ground level, the Cold War was growing ever chillier, Vietnam was reaching crisis point, there were strikes on the horizon, and students were revolting.

Something had to be done. Step forward three of the UK's most powerful cultural forces: The BBC, The Beatles, and The Post Office. Someone at the Beeb thought it would be a splendid idea to broadcast a two-and-a-half-hour live TV special worldwide using this spiffing new satellite communications technology.

The result was something called Our World, which went out on 25 June 1967, and was watched by perhaps 400 million people. You probably won't remember any of the worthy content from Canada, Australia and the US which was beamed around the planet via the UK's Goonhilly Earth Station in Cornwall and a constellation of primitive satellites. Except, perhaps, for one - the first public airing of a new Beatles ditty called *All You Need Is Love*, performed live from Abbey Road Studios in London and propagated globally.

That iconic moment alone probably sealed Our World's success. After that, said Wing, "the world just exploded". In a good way. The Post Office built a video switch at the tower site, and transmission of live broadcast rapidly became part of everyday life. At the same time, a community of production houses and other broadcast facilities appeared in the tower's shadow, alongside the advertising agencies. (This is one of the reasons why the surrounding area is particularly well-served by restaurants and bars, should a walk to Soho be too much for you.)

BT's broadcast network is a separate beast from the phone and comms network, linking production facilities around the world generally at 10Gbps, and these days overwhelmingly via fibre. While your cable network will be serving up a channel at 4Mbps, broadcasters will be working at 1Gbps.

Today, reckons Wing, "99 per cent of all content you see on TV at home has touched our network". Every Premier League football stadium has a fibre link back to the broadcast operation in the low-level building at the tower site, which can then switch content down to the appropriate broadcaster - which will include BT itself with its BT Vision plans. Meanwhile, channels are being switched through the tower either into the UK, or en route elsewhere. Wing said 3,000 channels are running through the tower at any time, and it handles about 18,000 hours of video per day.

Around 30 staff who have backgrounds in video broadcast networking as well as appropriate certifications in networking kit - mainly Juniper and Cisco - are running the site at any one time.

Wing said all signals are always sent via two geographically diverse paths to customers. It promises five-nines availability to its clients.

The tower has twin national grid power inputs, as well as twin UPS systems which would keep things up and running for 30 minutes, long enough for those ship engines to kick in. And, just in case, the site is mirrored at BT's Columbo House just over the river.

Depending on your point of view, this makes what happens at the tower even more critical to the national well-being - how many people may have been put out by the loss of voice calls back in the 1960s? Lose live Premiership matches and Comedy Central today? Well, let's hope the war room is still stocked up.

GPS
51.5214696, - 0.1389853

Post code
W1T 4JZ

Getting there
Goodge Street or Warren Street Tube.
Or just go to the West End and look up.

Entry
Not open to the public

The Kelvedon Hatch Nuclear Bunker
Essex

Ed Moore

Photo: Ed Moore

The bunker at the end of the world - in Essex

Open for 40 years, pointless for 39 of them...

Kelvedon Hatch is a superb example of absurdist geek life. Not only is the site technically very impressive, it is also completely useless and frequently prompts the question "what on earth were they thinking?". A tour reinforces this view as the experience now is as enjoyably peculiar as the history behind the place.

The Kelvedon Hatch bunker was built between 1952 and 1953 as part of the ROTOR project. This was a massive redevelopment of the UK's radar early warning system in response to Russia's successful test of a nuclear bomb and deployment of heavy bomber aircraft capable of reaching Britain. The contract was given to Marconi's Wireless Telegraph Company in what was apparently the largest ever government contract awarded to a UK firm.

The project established a hierarchy of 66 sites for Centimetric Early Warning (CEW) radar and Ground Controlled Interception (GCI) radar, with fighter command reorganised into six sectors controlled from four massive Sector Operations Centre (SOC) bunkers. ROTOR would use an upgraded radar system called the Type-80. As this was being prepared, the bunkers were constructed.

Kelvedon Hatch was built to be the Metropolitan Sector SOC bunker, of the largest "R4" design consisting of three underground levels. It is today the only complete R4 bunker still in existence and one of only two bunkers from the programme that can still be visited, the other being Anstruther in Scotland.

The construction project was a massive undertaking. After the hill was dug away, shock absorbers were first sunk 200ft (60m) into a bed of gravel. Then, on top of this, they poured a 100ft (30m) high concrete shell with walls 10ft (3.5m) thick, reinforced with tungsten rods every six inches.

So as not to interrupt building, braziers were kept burning night and day through the winter to keep frost away. Around the concrete, a Faraday cage was wired to keep out stray radio signals. Then came brickwork and waterproofing. Entrance tunnels were lined with 3ft (1m) of concrete and, hidden behind massive blast doors, bore holes were sunk and water tanks built. Then the earth was replaced.

Lastly, to "disguise" the site, a little bungalow was built over the entrance tunnel so no one would notice what it was. Presumably the 150 foot (46m) communication mast was not considered a complete giveaway.

So how long was Kelvedon Hatch usefully operational? About 12 months.

The newly developed Type-80 radar started to be installed in early 1953 and was found to be much more efficient than expected, with range doubling in some instances. This meant CEW and GCI sites could be combined, so massively decreasing the complexity of ROTOR.

With many fewer sites it was found that responding to alerts could be handled more quickly without referring up to the SOCs. The need for speed was given further impetus with the introduction by the Soviet Union in 1954 of their new Tupolev Tu-16a high-speed bombers, so Kelvedon as a useful command centre was finished.

It must have been obvious to everyone involved in the project that the massive cost of building the site couldn't be wasted, so it was converted; first into a civilian defence centre, then, later, as part of continuity of government plans into a Home Office "Regional Seat of Government". From 1967 this was as a Sub-Regional Headquarters and finally from 1985 it became the Regional Government Headquarters (RGHQ) for London.

In the event of nuclear war, the role of the RGHQs was to house the key government and military staff needed to run the country after the bombs had finished falling. Up to 600 personnel would be shut in and left isolated for up to three months or until it was safe to emerge. Everything they needed for food, water, power and air conditioning was provided in the complex while multiple communication networks linked them to the other centres and hopefully the remaining population outside. It would be grim but you'd be alive.

In 1992, Kelvedon Hatch was finally closed. Running costs were still £3m a year and the site had never been used in anger. At a closed auction, the Parrish family - who had originally sold the land for the base and still farmed the surrounding fields - bought it back. The family later opened it as the eccentric tourist attraction you can visit today.

There's a secret nuclear bunker somewhere near here
Photo: Ed Moore

The bunker is tucked away in the gentle Essex countryside, set a little way outside the small village of Kelvedon Hatch. How much the villagers knew about the facility I'm not sure, but it cannot have made them too happy to have such a sensitive government site next door.

Turning off the Ongar Road, you make your way along a winding access road through fields to the parking area. Keep going past the paintball arena, ropes course and quad bikes track that have sprung up around the complex and on to the bunker entrance itself, which is a nondescript bungalow.

The bunker was disguised with a small bungalow to cover the entrance way. Why? Who knows. Would a passing army just give it a nod and not look through the windows? My guess is a "committee" thought it a good idea.

Proceed up to the bungalow door and you'll find a small notice telling you to go right on in. What you won't find is any people; no entrance booth, no ticket collector, no tour guide, no security guard. No one. But they do have a lot of cameras pointing at you.

It's a little disconcerting given the usual experience of tourist attractions, but this is the Kelvedon way, so get used to it.

Once inside there's another notice saying to pay on the way out and just go pick up an audio guide, which you'll find lying in a big pile in the guardroom. Hit 1 and you're off. The audio guide is now the only way of finding your way about the complex and quite possibly the only way of ever finding your way out again, so pay attention and do what it says. Follow the arrows and hit new numbers when it tells you to.

The tour itself is in turns frightening, impressive and saddening. The initial entrance tunnel on the lowest floor is 100 yards of narrow and cooling bare concrete leading to the main and immense blast doors weighing over a ton each.

You'd know when these were shut you were gone for a good while.

Moving from room to room, you go past multiple communications rooms which were used over time and for reaching different destinations. The telephone exchanges – both manual and automatic – remain in situ as well as examples for radio communications and telex. Make your own pick but my favourites in this area are the BBC broadcasting suite and the famous "red telephones".

It's nice to know that the BBC would have been there trying to reassure and inform people even if most of the audience's radios would have no power... assuming they hadn't actually melted.

The small studio formed part of the Wartime Broadcasting Service but was held in reserve in case the main broadcasting suite at Corsham lost contact with the regions, in which case it would have sprung into action. The red telephones were used to inform police stations and council offices to sound the air raid warning once the bombs were on the way. There'd be no happy reason to pick one up so no wonder they were kept under cover - someone would get a shock if accidentally used!

Moving up a level you reach the main offices and control centres, plus accommodation rooms for the government chiefs. They may have been safe but looking at the prime minister's bedroom you hardly feel that life was good, even for them.

The rest of the bunker spans the impressive, to the mundane, to the pitiful. The power generators and air conditioners are huge rooms full of piping and engines, and Geiger counters everywhere remind you of the risks. Signs around the walls indicate the key operational areas. Judiciary, Home Office, Social Security, the Ministry of Agriculture & Fisheries and Fire Service all have desks. So do the Navy, Air Force and Army, but nothing for builders, doctors or farmers to actually start rebuilding the country.

Most mundane in the extreme has to be the stationery room where you had to justify the requisition of staples and paper. You even had to request a pencil holder for when it got too small to hold on its own.

The living quarters are pitiful. The tiers of bunk beds would have been used in shifts to save room. There are also chemical toilets for when the base was closed to save precious water, and worst of all, cardboard coffins for those who didn't make it. Boxed and bagged, the corpses could be pushed into corridors to await the all-clear.

Only at the end of the tour do you see any of the usual tourist paraphernalia. Racks of old uniforms for dressing up, a few war-themed items for sale and a restaurant for lunch or refreshments. Right at the end you'll find the honesty box for your entrance fee so even here it's a happy, help-yourself system.

You exit blinking into the unfamiliar sunshine through a hidden entrance from the top level. Walk back down and you're in the car park again.

Go try Kelvedon Hatch. An unbelievable amount of money was spent preparing for an eventuality that never arrived. But the site is a haunting reminder, an atmospheric experience of what life, for a terrified few, might have been.

GPS
51.672113, 0.257259

Post code
CM14 5TL

Getting there
Kelvedon Hatch is accessed from the A128 Chipping Ongar to Brentwood road at Kelvedon Hatch. Look out for the brown tourist signs, which is the first indication your trip will be fun, for they are marked "Secret Nuclear Bunker."

Entry
£7 adults, £5 for children - cash only. Group discounts offered

Online resources
http://www.subbrit.org.uk/rsg/features/rotor/
http://www.subbrit.org.uk/rsg/sites/k/kelvedon_hatch/
http://www.ringbell.co.uk/ukwmo/Page223.htm

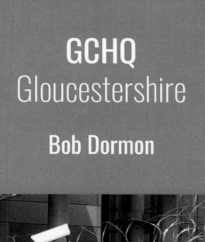

GCHQ
Gloucestershire

Bob Dormon

GEEK'S
GUIDE
TO BRITAIN

Photo: Bob Dormon

INSIDE GCHQ: Welcome to Cheltenham's cottage industry

"If this nerve centre didn't exist, neither would I"

For staff at the Government Communications Headquarters (GCHQ) in Cheltenham, there's an air of Fight Club about the place. The first rule of GCHQ is you don't talk about GCHQ.

It's a well observed tradition, even though there are road signs and a bus route directing you to this highly secret establishment, the nerve centre of Britain's communications surveillance operations.

The design of the doughnut-shaped building at Benhall has attracted a fair share of attention since its completion in late 2003. Indeed, if you take a look at the site from Google Earth, you might wonder if it Steve Jobs' plans for a new circular Apple building - a company that also likes to keep secrets.

Benhall is now the primary home of GCHQ and the majority of the service's 5,300 employees are based here. The organisation's own website describes itself as "one of the three UK Intelligence Agencies" and that it "forms a crucial part of the UK's National Intelligence and Security machinery". The other two are the Security Service (MI5) and the Secret Intelligence Service (MI6).

In years gone by, GCHQ in Cheltenham was spread over two sites a few miles apart: Oakley and Benhall. The Oakley site has largely given way to a housing development although some buildings remain, with the barbed wire fence rather menacingly separating it from a kids' play area on the new estate. While undoubtedly unintentional, this incongruousness does appear strangely Soviet – perhaps fitting, given that Cold War concerns became GCHQ's raison d'être in the 1950s.

I was born into a GCHQ family as my parents met there. As I write, it now occurs to me that if GCHQ didn't exist, neither would I. Spooky. I lived in a GCHQ house, too – purpose-built to accommodate the growing workforce – and I could see Benhall's satellite dishes from my bedroom window.

I worked there, too, and before I tread further along this telecoms taboo tightrope I should mention to our colonial cousins that what we have here is the equivalent of America's National Security Agency (NSA. For me, this association came in handy when applying for a US visa to visit a GCHQ colleague working for that ultra-hush-hush outfit. Mentioning those three initials at the US Embassy had my passport visa stamp in seconds.

Incidentally, I did ask the GCHQ press office if there was any chance of a tour of the building or even some publicity pictures of the interior. Admittedly, there was a bit of wishful thinking behind the former – there were employee family tours when the building was complete – but the answer was no. The polite response to the latter request was that pictures would be considered on condition the article could be viewed before publication. That's against our editorial policy, but chances are they've done that already.

I decided to take some photos myself, which are no more intrusive than those found on Google Streetview. It was only later that I spotted a "no photographs" sign, but as I was some distance away, I didn't notice it at first. I doubt I'd notice if I'm now being followed or having my communications tampered with as a result, but it would seem like a waste of time and of public money.

If you do go on a tour of 'Nam, taking pics aplenty up to the wire wouldn't be a very good idea. The security staff, many of who are ex-servicemen, take a dim view of this sort of thing.

As part of my research for this piece, I dug up Peter Freeman's 34-page booklet titled How GCHQ came to Cheltenham, which lays out a longer story than I'd anticipated. Freeman details the early years and the decision-making process that saw this sleepy Cotswold town – that for 75 years up to 1945 had a static population of 50,000 – undergo significant changes when GCHQ became operational. The population swelled by 20 per cent in the 1950s with a housing programme in place to support Cheltenham's new cottage industry: intelligence gathering.

Freeman remarks that the Ministry of Health's initial views were that "Cheltenham did not want civil servants and already had plenty of local employment". The Ministry of Works leaned on the Ministry of Health and consequently the town now breeds civil servants.

I was reading an exclusive edition of Freeman's work which features various handwritten corrections and additional detail courtesy of my mother - and she would know, being on the 1950s-era Foreign Office recruitment team based above the Ministry of Food bureau in Clarence Street, Cheltenham (rationing was still in operation in post-war Britain). Their task was to find the right stuff to staff Oakley and Benhall.

Yet how GCHQ came to Cheltenham owes more to what the Americans left behind after World War II than any strategic importance to the spa town's location. The Oakley and Benhall sites were purchased by the Ministry of Works in 1939 and building works began for the purpose of housing government departments if an evacuation from London's Whitehall became necessary. During the Blitz, some ministries had to move fast and ended up arriving before work on the temporary office blocks was complete. Each site had six of these utilitarian, single-storey, 12-spur buildings that, in total, clocked up more than 400,000sq ft ($121,920m^2$) of office space.

With the Blitz over, various departments returned to London, and the Americans, now involved in the war, found themselves at these two sites running a major HQ. The US SOS (Services of Support) dealt with logistics for the European Theatre of Operations and US Army (ETOUSA), and the buildings were used as offices for this communications hub. According to Freeman, the Americans arrived in secret and those coming from London had exclusive trains laid on to keep their movements under wraps. The railway staff at Paddington weren't so clued up though, and slapped up signs on the platform saying "US Forces To Cheltenham". As the Yanks dug in at 'Nam, they consequently installed a substantial network of landlines which remained after the war.

The clincher was when Cheltenham was visited by a staffer from GCHQ - then based at Bletchley Park near Milton Keynes - who knew of the site at Benhall, which was where the Ministry of Pensions had taken residence prior to an eventual move to Blackpool. Posing as an Admiralty official on a pensions fact-finding mission, he was granted a tour of the site and wrote up a favourable report of the place. Although there would be numerous inter-departmental and financial wrangles to follow, GCHQ eventually made its home in Cheltenham in the early 1950s.

Now established for more than six decades in Cheltenham, GCHQ has origins that go much further back. The Government Code and Cypher School (GC&CS) was formed in 1919 after World War I, its role being to assess security and coding methods within the government and develop improvements. Well, that's what the man in the street would be told: its other function was to analyse the communications systems Johnny Foreigner was using. Hence,

GCHQ, as it became known in 1946, has since been regarded as a "listening station". It's not the only one, but it is the most well-known in the UK.

Originally based in London, the bulk of GC&CS relocated Bletchley Park in August 1939, later moving to Eastcote in 1946 where there was an established GC&CS site with "analytic machinery" – the term "computer" had yet to catch on. Even though the wartime peak of 10,000 staff had now dropped to a few thousand, Eastcote wasn't in very good shape, was cramped and couldn't be expanded. Moreover, keeping it close to London – with the idea of a rapid redeployment farther afield if the threat of war loomed – was no longer practical. The cipher and communications technology now in use didn't take too kindly to being moved and, with the various preparations involved, could take up to six months to reinstall elsewhere.

Eastcote was too close to the capital and a suitable site that could function during times of war and peace became the new strategic focus. When the move finally came, the Eastcote facility transferred to Oakley in 1952. Benhall was earmarked for a consolidation of various radio stations a year earlier, but this was cancelled due to a number of concerns regarding space for the aerials and interference from nearby civil aviation communications sites at Elkstone and Winstone.

Even so, Benhall was established as a technical facility aided by its various workshops. In 1956, the Joint Speech Research Unit (JSRU was formed in Eastcote but eventually set up home at Benhall in 1978. This lodger unit produced rafts of papers on speech synthesis and analysis. It joined up with the Royal Signals and Radar Establishment in 1986 to become the Speech Research Unit, only later to be privatised in 1999. It is now called Aurix, owned by Avaya. Incidentally, the Speech Research Unit should not be confused with the Joint Technical Language Service (JLTS) that, if the ageing sign is anything to go by, is possibly still in residence at Oakley and undertakes a different role, focusing on translation and interpreting services.

Remember those temporary office blocks built in the 1940s? This implicit impermanence became a standing joke on both sites as each decade passed and they were still there. In fact, a few remain at what's left of Oakley that would now be entitled to a Civil Service pension.

I was installed for a time in one of these which was set up for experiments on magnetic tape, in varying conditions of humidity and temperature. The makeshift lab was nicknamed the "steam room" and I sat there, mostly on my own, creating environments in a chamber with water boiling away to supply the moisture and occasional blasts of carbon dioxide used to control the temperature. I'd monitor the results on a chart recorder and then type in a rather long-winded formula into a Honeywell scientific calculator to make some sense of it all.

You might wonder what on earth this had to do with the work of a listening station. In short, back then, a lot of tape recorders were used in various remote listening posts, and the idea behind this experiment was to discover what tape formulations worked best in different environments.

The block itself was pretty sparse, with aged linoleum flooring, big cast-iron radiators and draughty single-glazed windows. It would have been nice to have had a radio in there, but bringing in a tranny (that's a transistor radio) from outside wasn't permitted although sophisticated wireless equipment existed in abundance in other designated areas. Personal tape recorders and cameras weren't allowed, and you had to call in the official photographer to document any set-ups you felt deserved a snap. I'd be interested to know how the organisation deals with the abundance of smartphones today. Are they banned or is the place more trusting now, I wonder?

While Benhall is just a bus journey away these days, if you're keen to see the last remnants of Oakley, then you can either wend your way through the new housing estate or take a peek over a field from Aggs Hill. The latter is more of a challenge but can be made into an interesting diversion if you're a fitness fanatic or just fancy an easy way to get to the top of Cleeve Hill by car and admire the view along with the three aerial masts that can be seen clearly from the town.

If you've already done the housing estate Oakley drive-by, then the simplest way to get to Aggs Hill is to travel up Harp Hill where you'll be on the periphery of Cheltenham's most exclusive housing stock in Battledown. If you're a Tour de France enthusiast, cycling up Harp Hill should be a breeze, but the gradient of Aggs Hill is tough. Just keep going to the crossroads sign for Cleeve Common only. When you get to the end of the road you'll be under three sizeable antenna masts serviced by Arqiva, and you can stroll onto Cleeve Common – dog owners keep an eye out for sheep.

The splendour of the Cotswolds notwithstanding, if you did bike it this far, the real reward is whizzing back down Aggs Hill at a frightening rate with a nod to the remaining Oakley site entrance as you corner at the bottom... or hit the Hewletts Reservoir wall. The fun's not over; there's Harp Hill left

to descend – there used to be a hospital at the bottom, but not any more so take care. If you're still feeling sporty, or fancy a brew with a view, then The Rising Sun Hotel on Cleeve Hill is worth a visit. Alas, the High Roost Hotel on the same stretch closed in 2003 which was incidentally a US Army hospital during World War II. Oh, and don't forget, Cleeve Hill has a golf course too, where, for a fee, anyone can get their balls out and whack them off among the sheep.

When I worked at Benhall, which in the heyday of the two Cheltenham sites was focused on R&D – the job titles tended to be variants of scientific officer, technician (radio repair man) and radio operator. Being there also meant I spent most of my time in the new-ish 1970s building. The eternally dodgy lifts had puce panelling that was so intense you couldn't wait to get out, and some days you'd hear bagpipes playing in the quadrangle at lunchtime. This was no state occasion, just some chap engaged in windbag practice – optional for civil servants.

The labs themselves were spacious and well-equipped. Being a junior grade, I learned how to use sophisticated test equipment there but didn't see the attraction of playing *Star Trek* on the lab's DEC PDP-11 during breaks. It seemed like a lot of typing was going on but not much else. I'd be more inclined to have a go at building a guitar effects pedal instead; "working on a foreigner" being the phrase used to describe any pet projects or domestic repairs undertaken on site.

Benhall had its own immense stores and on your first day in this high-tech community you'd go through the various catalogues – some on microfiche – to find the equipment you'd need to build up your toolkit. It felt like being in a sweetshop but you'd need a senior officer's signature to get it all and some gear would be serialised too, so it wouldn't go astray - even the bloody leather tool bag. Going to stores was often welcome respite from the hum of the lab as nobody ever turned off equipment and even the oscilloscopes would add to the fan noise.

Typically, the lab would have its own reserve of resistors, capacitors and various silicon chips, which would be routinely checked. You could even put in an order to the stores using the Lamson tubes that featured on every floor. We're talking of the days before email here, and so messages were sent in small capsules along a pipe using compressed air. I remember seeing these in department stores when I was still in short trousers and was amazed to find technology hailing from the Victorian era in such a sanctuary of tech. What made matters worse was that some bright spark had decided to deploy a rectangular Lamson tube array. The thinking was that this would allow for larger payloads so you could get stores to send you back those resistors and capacitors using a Lamson tube. It would have been great if it wasn't for the fact the capsules were forever getting stuck. Circular objects in a round pipe = good. Rectangular objects in a flat sided duct = bad.

At about 10.15am and 3pm the official 15-minute tea break would be stirring into life. Some labs would have a proper sit-down in the corner while just a table and kettle would suffice for others. I remember once foregoing the usual chatter of current affairs and returning to my workbench with a cuppa during a break. The lab was now empty apart from me, when the Principal Scientific Officer (PSO) wandered in – the department's head honcho. He asked me where everyone was. I replied that they were having a "mass debate" in the tea room. He gave me a look of utter disgust and wandered off. It took a while for me to realise that I should have chosen my words more carefully, as even a communications expert misunderstood my mention of mass debating.

Surprising perhaps given the environment was equipped with Wayne Kerr knobs and tools aplenty.

Actually, the issue of misinterpretation reminds me of a situation my Dad described to me regarding context in intelligence gathering, which I'll come to in a moment. The late Steve Dormon spent a lifetime at Oakley; by comparison, I spent a lunchtime at Benhall. Oakley had different clerical and executive officer grades – fairly nondescript titles that veiled the true nature of the top-secret analysis many were involved in. While Benhall was all about hardware and technology, Oakley had admin and training at the front of the site, with beautiful minds working on intelligence analysis far from the madding crowd.

Benhall has changed beyond all recognition with all the temporary office blocks gone along with the 1970s-built multi-storey site that I knew. The environmentally friendly building was designed by US architect Gensler and is claimed to use 40 per cent less energy compared to conventional offices. The structure is 597ft (182m) in diameter, has 118,403ft^2 (11,000m^2) of aluminium roofing and 139,930ft^2 (13,930m^2) of glass.

Inside, there are cafés, bars plus a restaurant and a gym. An internal street is the hub of the site, joining up these facilities and the various departments. Being circular, you're no more than five minutes' walk away from anyone in the building. In the basement you can get around quicker,

as an electric goods train runs down there delivering stuff. An underground road handles more sensitive materials.

Other startling stats include the computer area that is said to be the size of the Royal Albert Hall. The doughnut frame used 250,000 tons of concrete, the electrical wiring covers 6,000 miles (9,656km) and BT laid 5,000 miles (8,047km) of cable and 1,850 miles (2,977km) of fibre. And to cap it all, the estimated total cost hit £1.2bn. Yet truth be told, the site is actually more interesting to view from aerial shots than from ground level, as it's a bit like a frisbee on a lawn: there's not a lot to see unless you're on top of it.

With this in mind, I took a night-time trip up to the top of Leckhampton Hill hoping a telephoto shot of the site would reveal some twinkling Stargate SG-1 charm. Apart from being farther away than I'd thought, it turns out to be quite difficult to see at night. A cluster of street lights hints at its whereabouts, but the building itself seems to be dressed in stealth bomber clothing, as it's virtually invisible. Cool.

A daytime pilgrimage is easy enough, as there are signposts everywhere. Finding the place is one thing, entering it is another – it's definitely members-only, having travelled the length of Hubble Road only to gaze upon the high-security car park. So, what next? Well, you could always go for a spot of flying at Gloucestershire Airport, Staverton on Bamfurlong Lane.

The airport used to be home to the beloved Skyfame Museum, but it has since expanded and become more of an aviation industry village. However, there is the revampedJet Age Museum that has relocated to the north of the airfield on part of the Meteor Industrial Estate. It's a shrine to early jet propulsion as the area is linked with the development of the Gloster Meteor – the first production jet aircraft based on Sir Frank Whittle's engine design.

If that sounds all too exciting for you, The Aviator café and restaurant at the airport has a full menu of grub to suit kids, veggies and carnivores alike. More importantly, the bar serves Wadworth's 6X which might settle your nerves to consider taking flying lessons at the Flying Shack just down the road. You can't miss it as there's an Avro Vulcan B2 XM569 cockpit in the car park. Oh, and keep an eye out for the type FW3/26 World War II pillbox on the roadside overlooking the airfield. But if terra firma and tinkering with cars is more your style, perhaps a trip to nearby Harry Buckland's scrapyard would suit? It's a local institution, having been going since 1935, so you never know what you might find there.

Oakley had its own bar too, and no doubt the thinking behind this was to keep lubricated chatter within the secure confines of the grounds. The fact that the place sold godawful keg bitter – I think it was Whitbread Tankard or Ind Coope Double Diamond – meant that most self-respecting drinkers ended up at The Bayshill Inn.. Not exactly local to Oakley but known for a decent pint of Wadworth's 6X. There was even a painted mural of regulars in there which included an ale fancier from GCHQ. No, you don't have to wear a burqa or similar to work there.

At one point I found myself at The Bayshill Oakley on a training course. During the lunch break I asked a security chap if I could go up the hill to visit my Dad. "Oh no, son," he scoffed, "you've not got clearance to go up there." Needless to say, bring-your-kids-to-work week has always been a bit of a damp squib for a lot of families in 'Nam.

Indeed, "how was your day?" tends to be a conversation killer for GCHQ employees too, but I do recall my Dad telling me about a course he attended that sounded a lot more fun than anything I'd been on. The gist of it was to do with context and how information could appear abstract when it lacked any reference points. The way this was demonstrated on the course was to play a muffled recording that sounded like people talking in the adjacent room. The group was asked if they could tell what was being discussed and none could. Then they were told that it was a conversation between a man and his tailor. The recording was played again and, armed with this reference, they could all understand it. I never found out if the mention of whether sir dressesto the left or to the right implied any political leanings.

Just for the record, it's worth mentioning that the good folk of GCHQ are not of a hive mind and don't all share the same political views. So don't think for a minute that snoopers' charters proposed by the government of the day are universally supported. While the technology may exist to follow a political whim, I'm sure most GCHQ bods would rather be tracking greater dangers than getting bored to death trawling through domestic emails or following misguided tweets.

Talking of politics, Thatcher initially proposed banning unions at GCHQ following the Civil Service strike in 1981, which some GCHQ personnel observed. I remember a handful of pickets at the site entrance, but it was all pretty passive. Still, Mrs T's thinking behind the ban was that this security service could not be compromised by strike action. There was quite a fuss, to put it mildly.

Somewhat naïvely, I was surprised by this as I had tried to join the union myself way before the ban arose. Despite phoning up the local union rep,

I didn't get the follow-up information I was expecting. The combination of my low wage (I wasn't exactly looking forward to paying the dues) and the mutual apathy that ensued meant I didn't become part of the union and was left with the distinct impression that there was no obvious urgency for members.

It's a pity this didn't work out though, as Thatcher compensated each GCHQ union member with a £1,000 cash payout for abandoning their respective trade union. The ban finally took effect in 1984 and 14 workers were sacked for refusing to relinquish union membership. It took until 1997 for unions to be permitted once more at the establishment.

I was there when the Falklands War broke out and although the conflict was fairly short-lived, the mood definitely changed during this period. Nobody was being jingoistic, and a single-minded seriousness prevailed. If anything, there was a sense of disappointment that we found ourselves in this situation, as part of the purpose of the organisation was to be so well-informed as a nation that conflicts could be avoided. Remember, GCHQ was there to monitor signals from around the world, as well as what was happening in Blighty.

Another pearl of wisdom from my Dad on this matter was that the Americans had warned us that the Argentines were gearing up for battle way ahead of their invasion of the Falkland Islands back in 1982 and that for some reason, the powers that be here in Britain had ignored this intelligence from our colonial cousins. I've no cause to doubt what I was told back then. History is littered with similar situations of intelligence being deliberately ignored or even sexed-up for political reasons.

Shielded and hidden, GCHQ hugs the flat horizon
Photo: Bob Dormon

Anyone who has taken an interest in the tales of secrecy at Bletchley Park during wartime will be aware that there is a "need to know" mindset, where people worked in separate teams without meeting or discussing their tasks with others. When I first heard this phrase at GCHQ I mistakenly thought it meant that one needsto know – like we were sharing stuff in some motivational way.

Of course, the emphasis is actually, do youneed to know? Oh well, I was not long out of school so such subtleties were initially lost on me. If people were coming and going in secret, it naturally wasn't obvious at all. I do recall the "cell" though, which I noticed one or two people emerging from occasionally. It was some kind of high-security broom cupboard, although it could have been like a Tardis inside, but I never found out. I guess I didn't need to know. Still, it's no surprise that places like that existed, whether for storing sensitive documents or working in a shielded environment. Maybe there was a Lamson tube in there going all the way to Cheltenham race course bookmakers.

The BBC managed to get a tour of Oakley before the demolition began and produced a couple of videos that include the high-security vaults, massive code-crunching computing areas and a backup power generator that could run the whole town.

While the mindset of secrecy is encouraged with good reason, it does have its drawbacks for those with ambition. I recall a few jaded souls who had stayed so long that, despite having exceptional talent, would find it difficult to leave because they couldn't tell a future employer on the outside what they'd been up to. So unless they could find a government job posting elsewhere, they were destined to remain residents of Hotel Gloucestershire: you can check out any time you like, but you can never leave.

On the other hand, high-flyers fresh from university would find they had an opportunity to shine, given the brain-tingling tasks they had to tackle and the resources at their disposal. Don't be shy of working there if you have the skills, but you might want to keep an eye on the calendar unless you're planning on being a lifer.

That being so, the secretive side of things can begin to seep into your thinking. Who's watching you? Surely, somebody must be from time to time as a routine security measure so you don't end up becoming vulnerable financially or in other ways.

Just how closely you are monitored can tease the imagination. On this point, my Dad would joke about voting Communist to see just how secret the secret ballot was. I don't suppose he ever put it to the test, but if you work there and feel lucky when the next election comes around, why not give it a shot?

Working there affected my thinking too, as it's only in recent years that I've stopped dreaming about returning to the place to embrace the technological challenges and achieve great things. Yes, I would finally have a crack at Star Trekand get to the Emeritus level, if only I could find a PDP-11 handy. Still, I picked up useful transferable skills there: fault tracing combined with being a dab hand with a soldering iron worked out very well when I found myself in London working in recording studios.

Naturally enough, the establishment has moved with the times. The intense efforts to monitor Cold War threats have largely given way to focus on the terrorism and cyber-security issues of today, as highlighted on the GCHQ website. Whatever you think about the secrecy of the place, the intelligence services endeavour to keep us safe. It was a motivating force for those who'd experienced World War II and went on to take jobs at GCHQ so this country wouldn't experience anything like that again.

I've no doubt it's a commitment that continues to this day: so far, so good.

GPS
51.898835, -2.120497

Post code
GL51 0EX

Getting there
A40, from Cheltenham or Gloucester

Entry
Not open to the public

Online resources
www.gchq.gov.uk/Pages/homepage.aspx
www.bletchleypark.org.uk
http://discovery.nationalarchives.gov.uk/SearchUI/

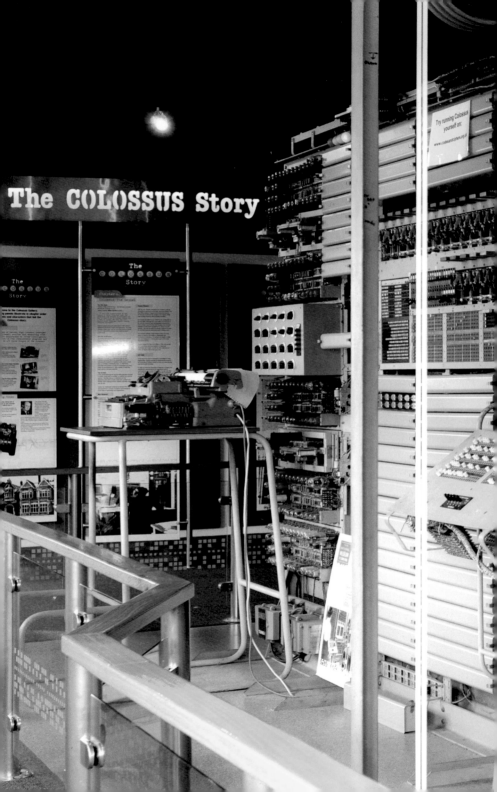

The National Museum of Computing
Milton Keynes

Gavin Clarke

Photo: Gavin Clarke

Rise of the machines, south of Milton Keynes

Computers make a noise at TNMOC

It's the sounds that get you: wheels spinning, processors squeaking, the furious hammering of teleprinters, and some 1980s synth.

Yes, computers really were this noisy – something you forget in an era when even the benign tap of the keyboard is giving away to the silent swoosh of finger on glass.

I'm at The National Museum of Computing (TNMOC) in Bletchley Park, near Milton Keynes, home to some of the oldest and rarest computers in the world. We have a working rebuild of World War II code breaker Colossus Mk II; schoolkids' favourite the BBC Micro; and one of the NeXT workstations created by Steve Jobs and his new company after he was booted from Apple - the machine picked by Tim Berners-Lee to help give birth to the worldwide web at CERN in the early 1990s.

It's near the end of my two-and-a-half hour TNMOC tour when the crescendo of microprocessors, sound chips and external electro mechanic sounds from these and many more computers finally hits me.

I'm not alone in appreciating these sounds: professionals are on the case, too. DJ Pixelh8, AKA Matthew Applegate, in 2009 caught, sampled and remixed the sounds of TNMOC with Obsolet, an album celebrating the mathematics, logic, code-breaking and crypto work of the machines and the museum.

TNMOC is filled with noises because, unlike some museums that place artefacts behind glass, and even in contrast to other computer museums around the world, TNMOC's objects work and TNMOC wants you – in most cases – to touch.

It's an appeal that transcends the generations, a fact attested to by increasing visitor numbers. Dads in their 40s, whose first computer was a ZX Spectrum, schoolkids getting their first taste of programming on a BBC Micro, pensioners of the World War II code-breaking generation and others in between are being lured by TNMOC.

My guide Andrew Spencer explains how it's not only the well-known kit that people can't wait to play with. Normally, it's the kids who love inputting their names into a lost classic Elliott 903 and have the Elliott's chattering teletype punch out their names on paper tape. On one particular trip, though, it was a senior IT executive who took command and who printed out no less than eight tapes. "You have some people who have never experienced that," Spencer recalls.

But this is modern, post-war stuff and our tour starts in Our Finest Hour: WWII, when the site TNMOC occupies was part of the UK Government's Code and Cypher School at Bletchley Park. At its peak, 12,000 mathematicians, engineers, military personnel and other staff toiled in three shifts around the clock, seven days a week to crack the encrypted communications of Nazi Germany's High Command.

TNMOC occupies Block H of Bletchley Park, a squat and angular bunker-like building constructed in 1944 from reinforced concrete to withstand bombing to house six of Bletchley's 10 Colossi. The other four were held in Block F, now demolished. Block F didn't go without a fight: tearing down the concrete walls took the hapless contractor who was awarded the job six months, and cost him two of his precious three wrecking balls, on a job he reckoned would take three weeks.

Our tour begins in two galleries dedicated to the Tunny and Colossus, built to crack communications encrypted using the Germans' Lorenz SZ42 cipher machine.

Lorenz messages were enciphered by adding a series of apparently randomly-generated letters to each letter in the original message, with random letters generated by a fiendish combination of 12 rotors. To decrypt, the receiving Lorenz added exactly the same obscuring letters back to the cipher text, also using its 12 rotors. Messages were communicated in International Teleprinter Code, where each letter of the alphabet is represented by a series of five electrical impulses; Morse code was not used.

The Tunny was built by a team from the Post Office Research Station without ever seeing a Lorenz, having worked out the machine's logical structure of circuits and rotors. Nobody actually knows for sure, but it is believed there were between 15 and 20 Tunnies operating at Bletchley during the war.

The Tunny produced the final decrypts, but that still left the job of working out the starting position of the Lorenz's rotors – a process that was being done by hand and thus took several weeks. Work was started on a new machine that led to the Colossus Mk I and Colossus Mk II, which cut the job to six hours.

The secret? Thermionic valves, the forerunner to solid-state components such as transistors and diodes in today's computers. Valves controlled a current in a vacuum-sealed glass tube and when arranged together could form a circuit. The Colossus program was entered through plug boards and switches, and the message was run on the tape across a series of wheels. The valves sped up the rate of numerical analysis on the messages.

Valves had been the idea of Tommy Flowers, an electrical engineer with the General Post Office (GPO), which ran the UK's phone services. Flowers had been working with valves since 1934 and argued they possessed the necessary power and reliability. The first Colossus in 1943 used 1,500 valves; Colossus II in 1944 used 2,500 valves.

If you visit the museum, you won't be seeing the original Tunny and Colossus - they were destroyed after the war on the order of the top brass as Lorenz machines began falling into the hands of the Soviets. The machines on display are working rebuilds, constructed from scratch by volunteers working from a handful of old photos, circuit diagrams and – in the case of the Colossus Mk II – the memory of Flowers himself.

The Tunny is big, measuring 7.5ft high (2.286m) and 4ft (1.21m) wide and about one foot deep, but the Colossus is even bigger: 7.5ft high (2.286m), 15ft wide (4.5m) and 6ft (1.82m) deep and. The Colossus Gallery housed Colossus machine number nine.

How did the Tunny and Colossus work?

First, the teleprinter code came in over the air – that's the wibbly wobbly high-frequency radio noise you'll hear filling the air of the Tunny gallery when you take the tour. Back in the war, this noise was filtered and converted by hand to paper tape that was stuck together to make a loop that fed over a series of spinning wheels and was read optically.

The Colossi were programmed to conduct a statistical attack on the code to work out the probability of what each letter meant and thereby determine the Lorenz wheels' start position. This attack was mounted using the valves chewing the algorithm they'd been fed.

Listen carefully, and above the crazy whirling and reeling of wheels and whooshing of tape on the Colossus Mk II you can also detect a hypnotic tick, tick, tick as the wheels complete a revolution; they spin at 40 miles per hour, reading 5,000 characters per second. Colossus could read 10,000 characters a second, but at that speed the tape would break, so 5,000 was the limit. Each click is a single revolution, with each revolution a statistical attack on the message. So, what you're hearing is computing in action.

TNMOC's restored IBM 1130, once one of IBM's cheaper systems
Photo: Gavin Clarke

Was it worth it? Colossus played a pivotal role in the D-Day invasion: signals between Hitler and Field Marshal Rommel were cracked using the Colossus Mk II to reveal Hitler had bought the Allies' deception that the invasion of Northern Europe was coming to Calais in 1944. He overruled Rommel's request to shift elite Panzer troops down to Normandy, a move that could have turned the invasion into another bloody defeat like the Gallipoli landings of World War I. The message was reviewed in Block D, at Bletchley Park by – we're told – "very senior members of command".

All told, TNMOC reckons 63 million characters of "high-grade" German communications were decrypted by 550 people on the 10 Colossus computers.

The atmosphere today in the Colossus gallery feels like some stately home filled with the sound of the mechanical ticking and gentle spinning of antique time pieces. However, it wasn't like that when the Women's Royal

Naval Service (WRNS, colloquially known as Wrens) ran the machines. The noise was the same but the room was hot, humid and - occasionally - hazardous.

This gallery housed a single Colossus machine that was never turned off. The machine ran 24 hours a day and seven days a week because – Flowers believed – as long as the valves were left powered on, they could operate reliably for very long periods, especially if their heaters were run on a reduced current.

It's assumed the room's doors remained shut and windows closed owing to the blanket of secrecy that smothered Bletchley, and also because of the night-time blackout that everybody had to observe during the war.

That meant things got hot and humid. In true stiff-upper-lip fashion, the brass permitted the Wrens to remove their jackets and roll up their sleeves as a concession to these uncomfortable working conditions. They were the only Wrens allowed this level of undress.

Rebuild of the Tunny - the machine that cracked the German high-command's comms
Photo: Gavin Clarke

Once, a leak flooded the room housing Colossus No 9 with water, something that would have been dangerous to machine and the Wrens - for different reasons. This flood is believed to be the source of a persistent myth that water was poured on the floor to try to keep temperatures in the room down.

We leave the dedicated galleries and head to the post-war world, and run into more valves: 829 of them, to be precise. That tungsten-coloured glow represents the computing power running the world's oldest working digital computer: the Harwell Dekatron Computer, or WITCH, recently rebooted following a four-year renovation.

The WITCH is really a 2.5-ton calculator that ate numbers and spat out answers to complex calculations for the Atomic Energy Research Establishment. It was meant to be more reliable than a team of mathematicians punching away at calculating devices.

Past the WITCH, things start to get more hands-on as we hit TNMOC's three Elliotts, from Elliott Automation. The Elliotts were mass produced in the 1960s and 1970s, with hundreds of units sold to business and academia, before the company was subsumed into ICL, GEC and British Aerospace through a series of deals.

The Elliotts boasted several unusual features and a number of firsts. The 803 is believed to be the first all-transistor computer used in the UK. It featured brand new magnetic cores for logic gates as well as for memory – of which it packed a mighty 20Kb. The 803 used magnetised 35mm film tape from Kodak for storage, and boasted the ability to plug into the mains power supply because, unlike its predecessors, it had dispensed with the need for a special power supply that juiced up the voltage.

It's four cabinets' worth of computer, with a reader and copier, an operator console – no monitor – and a plotter added to the set-up in the 1960s. Next to the plotter lies a sheet of paper with a picture of a Kingfisher produced by the Elliott that looks like it was made on a kids' Spirograph - proof the Elliotts are still in use at TNMOC and evidence that a large number of Elliotts were used in design work, as well as for crunching numbers.

Peek inside a clear-sided cube on top of the 803 and you can see the 20Kb of solid-core memory; a matrix of criss-crossing wires intersected by 160,000 hand-made rings that changed to zero or one when a current was applied. Retrieving data meant scrolling through the Elliott's 35mm magnetic storage tape, which could take up to 15 minutes.

Despite this, the 803 was nowhere near powerful enough to run business-critical operations like wages, stores and sales that big companies needed. This was handled by punch-card systems, an example of which is housed in a TNMOC room. It looks like the skeletal remains of a Terminator machine.

It's the Elliott 903 where things get noisy. Elliott Automation added the paper tape reader and teletype to the 803. TNMOC has plugged in a monitor to this beast so you can view things electronically. The 903 adds a further 8K of memory while the processor makes a dry squeaky sound – like an old wheel in need of oiling.

In an age when you didn't have monitors to see what was wrong, engineers added such sounds to determine how the machine was working, Spencer says. Engineers would listen for variations; silence, it seemed, was a sign things had gone wrong.

Opposite the Elliotts are 20 washing machine-shaped metal cabinets. Meet the ICL 2966, the largest of TNMOC's machines so far, with a mighty 7GB of disk storage. Machines like the 2966 were used in large public and private operations in the 1970s and 1980s. TNMOC's beast ran billing, payroll, and general accounting for TARMAC Quarry Products in Wolverhampton between 1985 and 1999.

Storage in this room-sized squatter was tiny but performance was not: storage media consisted of massive ceramic discs covered with a magnetic coating and capable of holding 200MB each. Accessing a specific piece of data meant entering a query into a terminal that told you which disc held the data. The disc was then loaded into a reinforced cabinet, weighing two tons, and spun up to 1,000 RPM.

Both the drums and buildings hosting them had to be specially reinforced because they'd vibrate while running at full power, while the discs had a habit of breaking free. "One guy told me a story of it punching though the wall and into the River Thames," Spencer says.

Arranged around the ICL beast and its 200MB disc is a display of storage media, showing how things have shrunk while capacity has grown.

Now, though, we get personal as we enter a gallery of PCs from the 1980s: among them, Sinclair Spectrums, BBC Micros and Amstrads, and an IBM 5150 of the kind that became Time magazine's Person of the Year in 1981.

Here the sounds are more rounded than the metallic punching and dry squeaking of the Elliott: they are uniform and layered – an aural comment on the explosion in PC ownership during that decade and the sheer number of different types of PCs that were available. TNMOC seems to be piping in some soft '80s synth music, too. It's here you can get hands-on and either relive old memories of key-tapping or show the kids how a program started by loading your code from a cassette tape.

TNMOC is a work in progress and the PC gallery is the last of its refurbished areas. In the unfinished room next door we find business computers in a holding pattern, waiting to be displayed properly.

BBC Micros, first love for many and now used by today's student coders
Photo: Gavin Clarke

If the gallery we left behind was for the consumer, this is all business. Among the machines here is a Xerox Star, whose program takes a full six hours to load. The machine is often left turned off, we're told, because it's time to go home by the time it's up and running. A NeXT Cube workstation and a NeXT Station mini-computer complete the room's artefacts. These are machines of legend, thrice blessed by the digital gods.

First, they were created by the hand of Steve Jobs at NeXT Computer, the company he founded after he was booted out of Apple in 1988 following a boardroom insurrection. Second, it was a NeXT that Tim Berners-Lee used at CERN to run the world's first web browser – the Cube is one of CERN's machines, but not, alas, the actual example used by Berners-Lee himself.

The NeXTSTEP object-oriented, multitasking operating system these machines run became the basis for Apple's iOS when Apple bought NeXT – and Jobs – for $429m in 1996.

"People can use these machines," Spencer tells me. "And people do use this one."

Alas, romance is kinder than history. Even in those heady days, people cooed over the NeXTs despite the fact they were ugly by the aesthetic of today's silver Macs. Jobs, venerated today as an angel of design, was clearly going through his "black casing" phase. Also, few people could actually use a NeXT, as most applications were being written for Windows instead.

After the NeXT gallery you head into a room of 12 BBC Micros. Here, students and school pupils alike learn BASIC on these machines, 1.5 million of which shipped during the 1980s. Kids here hack a snake-like game.

"For most school students, it's their first taste of programming," Spencer tells us. Up to five groups a day are coming in to pound the Micros' chunky brown keys - and it's not just kids: senior citizens from the University of the Third Age, ex-London-Underground IT staffers and Danish maths teachers have been filing in, too.

There's more at TNMOC, but our time's up. There's a room dedicated to ARM, which sprung out of BBC Micro-makers Acorn. Today Acorn dominates smart phones, air-traffic radar control, those Terminator-like hole-punch machines and a new software gallery.

On your way out we stop by the TNMOC shop and café, where you can pick up t-shirts, books, mugs and trinkets - including chunky brown keys of cannibalised BBC Micro keyboards bearing your favourite letter or command. Café refreshments are solid - soft drinks and biscuits, teas and coffees from a machine.

Further afield is Milton Keynes, where you can catch up on shopping and the usual diversity of high-street refreshment. To the east are the spires and fens of Cambridge. If you want to linger overnight and recharge locally, there's a handful of places to stay, including the Bletchley Park B&B. Again, Milton Keynes has more to choose from with the City Central B&B, and Double Tree Milton Keynes. There are more choices in Cambridge.

TNMOC is a museum that doesn't stand still. After two skilled rebuilds (Tunny and Colossus) and one reconstruction (WITCH), a fourth project is now underway on EDSAC, built by Maurice Wilkes. EDSAC became the blueprint for the world's first business computer, the Lyons Electronic Office (LEO) in 1951.

And while you can't – and won't - use these particular systems, TNMOC has an expanding culture of touch: at the time of writing this meant an exhibition on computer music where you can experiment with music software on PCs from the 1980s.

The computers in your life might be getting quieter, but those from our past aren't staying silent, it seems, thanks to TNMOC.

GPS
51.998794,-0.743705

Post code
MK3 6EB

Getting there
By train: between 30-50 minutes from London Euston to Bletchley. By car: between the A5 and A421, north of London.

Entry
Fee is £7.50 per person, £5 for concessions and no charge for children 5 and under. Entering Colossus and Tunny galleries only is £3, or £2 for concessions. TNMOC is free to members. Insight Guided Tours are priced at £12.50 with £10 for concessions. The Colossus and Tunny galleries are open daily; the rest of TNMOC is open every Thursday, Saturday and Sunday afternoon from 12pm.

Online resources
www.tnmoc.org

National Lift Tower
Northampton

Tony Smith

Love in an elevator.... testing mast: The National Lift Tower

El Reg shows where you can go and get truly shafted

The Tower rises above the flat plain of the Nene valley near Northampton - for centuries home of Britain's shoe industry but these days better known as the home town of 11th Doctor, Matt Smith, cult comics creator Alan Moore and *El Reg* operations manager Matt Proud - like some kind of latter-day Barad Dûr or Orthanc.

The sinister cylinder, reaching 419ft (128m) up from the ground, isn't cut from black stone, but formed from concrete as grey as the Midlands sky. Its smooth surface is punctuated only by a series of viewports, black against the smoky wall (they hardly warrant the word "window" with its connotations of illumination). The peak terminates with a series of jutting steps and gaping maws like some massive crenelation from which a Dark Lord might gaze forth across his domain.

In fact, this monument to 1970s design and 1980s construction was built for far more mundane purposes. Now called the National Lift Tower, it was originally raised by the Express Lift Company for testing elevators before installation, and for training the engineers who would tackle the lifts' maintenance.

Express had been manufacturing lifts in Northampton since 1909 when one of its founding firms, Smith Major & Stevens, moved out of London and established the Abbey Works, so called because it was constructed on the site of a Medieval monastery. Construction work on the factory was frequently interrupted by the unplanned exhumation of many a cenobite's skeletal remains.

Like the monks of the Augustinian Abbey of St James, Express has long since shuffled off its mortal coil. Its original owner having gone to the great winching room in the sky in the mid 1990s, the NLT is now no longer used for testing elevator rigs before they go into buildings, but rather for R&D across industry and academe. These days it's as likely to welcome a group of weekend abseilers as a team of elevator maintenance trainees.

Located just a conversion kick from Northampton Rugby Football Club's Franklin's Gardens ground - go, Saints! - the Tower's facilities include six lift shafts of varying heights and speeds, one of which is a 30.4ft (100m) high-speed tube with a theoretical maximum speed of 32ft per second (10 meters per second). The Tower also has a drop-test facility with a height of 98ft (30m) and a lifting capacity of 10 tons (10,000kg). The building also encompasses what the current operators sinisterly describe as a "void used for research" - it's 252ft (77m) deep.

I peered through the foot-diameter hole used to send smaller objects on their way down, and it's not a view for those with a fear of heights. The tower isn't generally open to the public, but I was kindly shown around by Ed Wright, one of the three-man team that now runs the NLT. In a former life, Ed was a server wrangler, and one of his many tasks as the Tower's administrator and factotum is implementing the facility's IT network and AV set-up.

When the NLT partnership took over the Tower five years ago, there were almost no facilities remaining within the concrete shell. The building wasn't derelict, but in the years since Express Elevators' collapse, the firm's subsequent acquisition by US lift colossus Otis and the eventual sale of the land on which the Abbey Works had been established, the Tower saw little use.

Not so now. Ed and partners Pete Sullivan - the building's owner - and Matthew Fenn had the Tower reconnected to the grid and other key utilities, fitted out workshops and training rooms, and began to pitch the building to the elevator world as a unique research and development facility in the UK. The NLT is currently being rigged with the latest in winching systems - one of which will allow ascent speeds more than 55.7ft per second (17 metres per second) or more, using a gearless magnetic mechanism and microprocessor control - and the buffers used to arrest carriages descending at such high speeds. It's getting a hi-tech hydraulic lift system too.

And it's not just the lift industry that has expressed an interest in the old Express tower, says Ed. Boffins and engineering companies from across Europe now use the Tower to test and evaluate safety systems for technicians working at great heights - and miners working at great depths, since the Tower's voids can simulate shafts descending into the Earth's crust just as well as they can the side of a mast supporting a power-generation turbine.

If it's dangled or dropped from a great height, or has to move up and down the space in between, the Tower has room to test it.

And its cheaper, says Ed, briefly donning his sales hat, than specially rigging up a tower crane to do it.

This is today - back in the mid 1930s, elevator people had to make do with Express Lifts' first tower, a 59ft (18m) job rising up through the roof of the Abbey Works plant. This erection satisfied Express engineers' needs for the following 40 years, but in the late 1970s it was decided they had to have something rather larger - a building tall enough, in point of fact, to give high-speed lifts the space not only to accelerate up to speed but to run for a suitable distance and then decelerate and come safely to a stop.

Planned with an operational life of 25-40 years, the new tower would contain not only test shafts each running at various speeds, but service lifts and training rigs for maintenance crews and rescue personnel. Should the power be lost, workers could ascend and descend the Tower using a staircase running up the full, 20-storey height of the building, lit by daylight, and zigg-zagging its way up through the structure.

The Tower's design, by architects Stimpson and Walton of Northampton, was finalised in 1980 and work began shortly afterwards, with London-based Tileman and Co handling the construction work. Raising the edifice took just over two weeks, with concrete being poured into a series of moulds which would rise up on the dry concrete below as the tower's height increased. The peak rate of growth: 300mm an hour, or 7.2 metres (23.6ft) a day.

Pausing only to curse Windows 8's Modern UI - once an IT pro, always an IT pro - Ed shows me the company's collection of photos taken during the Tower's construction.

The Tower was built on a 78.7ft (24m) wide, three-metre thick concrete "raft", set down in two separate pourings. The raft allows the 4,000-ton (4,064,188kg) Tower to float on the soggy soil prevalent in these parts. Ed describes the set-up as a "pencil balancing on an aspirin". From the raft, the tower tapers through roughly half of its height before rising as a cylinder from then on, its diameter shrinking from 47.9ft (14.6m) at the base to 27.8ft (8.5m). The tapering helps the Tower withstand the buffeting of the wind.

The Tower's unusual peak helps too, acting to dampen lateral movement in high winds. The trick was to leave the concrete outer cover off the upper section, exposing the lift shafts and walkways to "reduce the suction force on the leeward side by virtue of the through-holes and irregular shape breaking up the vortex effect", as Express Lifts' own description of the facility puts it.

Dominating its surroundings, the tower is topped by an unusual peak to cope with high winds. Photo: Tony Smith

Above and below are glass-sealed decks, but the top level is open to the elements. It provides a splendid view of Northamptonshire and surrounding counties, but most of the folk who go up there these days immediately go sliding down the outer skin on ropes after climbing out over a gantry that originally held a BT point-to-point microwave transceiver. A second dish, aiming south, is still there, but unused.

On completion, the Tower was "one of the tallest lift testing towers in the world" and one of only two of its kind in Europe. It was formally opened by the Queen on 12 November 1982.

Express Lifts itself was formed in 1928 through the merger of Smith Major & Stevens (SMS), GEC Elevators and Easton Lifts, though the firm could trace its history back to the 1770s thanks to SMS's long history as a maker of hoisting gear.

In the early 1990s, Express merged again, this time with fellow UK lift company Evans, but the partnership was not successful and the combined company soon went bust. It was acquired by US elevator giant Otis, which still uses the Express & Evans brand in some installations.

Otis may have been keen to keep the brand, but it wasn't interested in the Tower. The American company quickly sought to capitalise upon its acquisition by selling off the land on which the Abbey Works was situated. The area was soon in the hands of property developers, who wanted to pull the Tower down. The building's safety was called into question, and scare stories appeared in which it was claimed it was suffering from "concrete cancer".

Local protest saved the Tower from demolition, even though the Express Abbey Works was razed to the ground to make way for the housing estate in which the Tower sits, more or less in the centre. Clearing the factory site at least finally allowed, in 1999, for a proper excavation of the Abbey by Northamptonshire Archaeology.

The Tower is now a Grade II-listed building. As for the "concrete cancer", it's true, there were some parts of the building with a high level of ironstone in the mix, leading to rust staining on the exterior, but Ed and his colleagues were able to have them cut out and refilled, so that key modern building regulations could be met.

There's no reason, then, that the National Lift Tower - not merely a monument to Britain's modern industrial heritage but also, pleasingly, a working building once more - won't gaze out across the Nene valley for many, many years to come. It can now continue to do its bit for the British light industry renaissance, at once defining Northampton's skyline and giving the thousands who pass by on the M1 something to ponder: "What the bloody heck is that for?"

GPS
52.238627, -0.922070

Post code
NN5 5FH

Getting there
From Junction 15A of the M1, take the A5123 north and then the A5076. Turn right onto the Weedon Road (A4500) towards Northampton town centre. Turn right onto The Approach, which runs right up to Tower Square.

Northampton can be reached by train from London Euston or Birmingham New Street.

Entry
Not open to the public

Hanslope Park
Milton Keynes

Tony Smith

Photo: Tony Smith

Hanslope Park: Home of Britain's 'real-life Q division'

The Buckinghamshire haunt of spooks, BOFHs and boffins

Hanslope Park sits just outside the small, quiet North Buckinghamshire village of Hanslope. I grew up there, and the Park and its occupants would always be mentioned by conversing grown-ups in suddenly hushed tones. Who might be listening? Other villagers were quietly pointed out with the words: "You see him? He works at the Park, he does."

Today the site might well fail to attract the attention of passing motorists, but in the 1970s and 1980s, while you couldn't see much of the facility itself thanks to the thick growth of trees and bushes that surround it, the plantations of sinister masts that dotted the nearby fields rather gave the game away. They're mostly gone now, pulled down in the 1990s to be replaced by more sophisticated spy satellite pick-ups.

Hanslope Park, once the scene of notorious murder and suicide, has long been home to spooks - and, it's claimed, not just of the corporeal kind.

The site is now officially named Her Majesty's Government Communications Centre (HMGCC), but the Park and the small, undistinguished stately home at its centre were acquired after World War II by the Foreign Office, which soon established a listening post there. The locals widely believed the station was tuning in to Russian transmissions, perhaps giving us an advantage over other Britons should the balloon ever go up. There was talk of nuclear bunkers and a secret way from the Park to the M1, which passes by just a kilometre away.

The all-seeing eyes of Google Earth or Bing satellite photography reveals no such roadway. Unless, of course, it's underground...

Curiously, it was reported in the 1980s that a chap who claimed his car had broken down on the M1 late one night, was picked up trying to enter Hanslope Park. He said he had made a beeline for the facility's bright yellow sodium lights in the hope of finding assistance. He would have had better luck - and less tired legs – had he tried either of the two farmhouses between the motorway and the Park.

During the 1970s, locals who worked at the Park might, when asked, mutter something about the Foreign and Commonwealth Office, a line that suggested they were really little more than clerks from the days of Empire (no one had thought of the "I could tell you but I'd have to kill you" gag back then). It was called the Diplomatic Wireless Service, and it wasn't hard to imagine messages coming in announcing coups d'étatand incidents in far-flung capitals.

Not that the intelligence community connections were unknown, even if then not officially confirmed. Hanslope is only 20 miles or so from the south Milton Keynes town of Bletchley, home to a better-known Park with a shady wartime history.

As the HMGCC itself puts it: "We're a short drive from the thriving towns of Milton Keynes and Northampton. We also benefit from good transport links, with Milton Keynes station only 35 minutes to London Euston on a fast train." The local church, St James - described by architectural historian Nikolaus Pevsner as one of the finest spires in the country, and easy to locate at ground level for many miles around - forms part of the agency's logo. It is "involved in fascinating, challenging work of national importance".

Or, as *The Guardian* newspaper once put it, a place: "Where teams of scientists – real-life versions of Q, the fictional boffin of the James Bond films – devise technical aids for the Foreign Office, MI5 and MI6".

According to the Foreign Office, Hanslope Park maintains a high-definition "secure video conferencing link" called Secview with Downing Street and the Foreign Office.

Even the HMGCC admits its boffins: "Work across the whole product lifecycle, from research and design to development and production. We deliver bespoke communications systems, applications, hardware and software to meet our customers' unique requirements". Hanslope Park is, the organisation that runs it modestly claims, "a creative powerhouse and centre of excellence".

"Across the site, there are a number of labs and teams made up of professionals from a wide variety of backgrounds, forming a melting pot of ideas where innovation is the main objective. From software developers and mechanical engineers, to systems specialists, electronic experts and even a fully functioning manufacturing plant, we have a huge range of professionals on board - including our vital corporate and support people."

HMGCC's own "come and work for us" video shows parabolic satellite uplink antennas, banks of black supercomputers and, this being Blighty, a canteen selling tea and buns. The video shows the Park's mod cons - including a gym for the staff, or perhaps trainee spies - and no sign of the 18th century manor house, once home to Squire of Hanslope Park, Edward Hanslope Watts in the late 19th century and early 20th.

On Sunday, 21 July 1912, Watts, 67, and his wife Edith were walking back from the village and the morning's church service. As they neared their home - they were just a few dozen yards from the Park's former gatehouse - two shotgun blasts rang out and Watts collapsed to the ground, blood gushing from a head wound. One of the two shots hit him in the back, though it's not known whether the blast was intended for the Squire or his wife. She was reported to have seen the shooter.

A spot to die for – scene of a murder and suicide at Hanslope Park
Photo: Tony Smith

The shots attracted the attention of others from the Park. Another shot was heard. Shortly afterward, the body of William Farrow, the Squire's head gamekeeper, was found in the bushes to the left of the road. Farrow was dead, his shotgun resting against his body. He had fired the weapon into his own mouth.

Edith was related by marriage to General Sir John French, who, two years later, would lead the British Expeditionary Force to France and Belgium at the start of the First World War. The story of the shooting was written up by *The Times* and the *Daily Mirror*.

Why did Farrow fire on the couple? At the inquest held the following day, the jury found him guilty of wilful murder. It was said he had taken revenge after being told by Watts that his services were no longer required.

The event was soon forgotten, but from then on there were tales of ghostly sightings and experiences in and around the manor house and on the road to Hanslope. Whose spectre haunts the spooks of Hanslope Park? William Farrow? His victim, Squire Watts? Or Watts' distraught wife, Edith? We will never know, though a neighbour of mine in the village once claimed to have been grasped on the shoulder while at work in the manor house. No one was there when he turned round, but they're a rum lot up at the Park, eh, Mr Smiley?

These days the only tapping to be heard at Hanslope Park is the rattle of keyboards and the staccato Morse on the HMGCC promo video. With the arrival of the HMGCC moniker, the site has been expanded considerably in the past decade or so. There are visibly more buildings than there were when I used to cycle past as a kid, though in summer time it's hard to see past the surrounding greenery.

Some of the extra space is said to be occupied by MI6's Technical Security Department (TSD), but in the information age you clearly need more staff to go over the data picked by the likes of GCHQ Cheltenham and RAF Menwith Hill, North Yorkshire than you do for producing spy gadgets.

And not just the latest information. Hanslope Park is home to the SIS's archive, if we're to read between the lines of a 2009 BBC Radio 4 series about MI6 called *Century in the Shadows*. It noted the presence of a "cavernous vault" of historical SIS information "somewhere just outside London". Two years later, confirmation of sorts came from the Foreign Office itself in a document describing the movement of FO colonial papers to a trove in Hanslope Park.

Much of HMGCC's kit – those bits not developed internally, that is - comes from HP, which was contracted by the Foreign and Commonwealth Office in 2005 to design and build the next generation of the FCO's "Firecrest", the system that connects Britain's embassies and other diplomatic outposts around the world. Signed in 2005 the "Future Firecrest" deal was worth £401m.

And it's appropriate, don't you think, that HP (Hanslope Park) was kitted out by HP (Hewlett-Packard).

Providing a home for the technology was a new "secure hub for our global Information and Communications Technology (ICT) infrastructure", construction of which began in 2005. Part of it was the FCO's "new centre for cyber security", opened in November 2010. The ICT housing is known simply as "Building 38".

The FCO also maintains a "goods store" at Hanslope Park. These are maintained by FCO Services, the commercial wing of the FCO, which sells "secure" IT and communications - satellite, landline and mobile - testing services plus "perimeter and protective security" services.

"With over sixty years' experience as the UK National Authority for Counter-Eavesdropping (UKNACE), we've got the technical means to detect or prevent eavesdropping devices compromising the security of your site," its website says. It also developed the Government Secure Application Environment (GSAE) cloud computing infrastructure.

Still, it can't be that hush-hush when so many FCO operatives mention their involvement on their LinkedIn pages.

GPS
52.106228, -0.809405

Post code
MK19 7BH

Getting there
Hanslope Park is situated four miles north of Milton Keynes and 10 miles south of Northampton, between junctions 14 and 15 of the M1.

Entry
Not open to the public.

Cruachan Power Station
Argyll and Bute

Bill Ray

GEEK'S
GUIDE
TO BRITAIN

Boffins, Tunnel Tigers and Scotland's world-first power mountain

The hollowing heroes who reversed nature

In the middle of a Scottish mountain is a man-made cavern 90 metres high and 36 metres long - tall enough to stuff an entire cathedral in its belly - which is only accessible through a kilometre-long rock tunnel. This is the home of the Cruachan Power Station.

In 1921 - with one world war down and one to go - the British government surveyed its mountains with a view to generating hydro-electric power. The survey established that Cruachan, near Oban on the west coast of Scotland, would make an ideal site for storing power - if only the technology existed to make it practical.

One world war later, the technology had arrived. Within a decade, nuclear power was generating an overnight excess in need of storage, so in 1959 they broke ground to build the world's first reversible-turbine power station, which essentially uses large amounts of water to store excess energy.

That power station now comprises an artificial loch, dammed with 200,000 tons (203,209,382kg) of concrete and storing 7 gigawatt-hours' worth of water - 22 hours supply with a 12-hour reserve. That water drops down a sloping 305 metres into four turbines housed in the middle of the mountain, where we're allowed to visit them.

The idea is simple to explain, rather harder to realise: water falls from the loch above through turbines to generate electricity, 440MW of it at peak, but at night the same turbines are turned (using excess power) to push the water back to the top loch again, making the whole thing a huge storage battery designed to buffer between the constant generation and variable consumption of electricity.

Not that you'd know it driving past Cruachan. The only signs that give away what lies beneath are the suspicious number of pylons - and a large sign pointing visitors towards the centre. Once you've got there, you can buy tea and cake, peruse postcards and novelties, press buttons in the exhibition and board the minibus which takes visitors to the heart of the mountain.

Cruachan's biggest problem in becoming a hydro plant was the lack of upper loch from which water could flow. The mountains had a nice valley but it drained neatly into Loch Awe, so the first order of business was to build an enormous dam. That took two years, thanks to the remote location and inclement weather. Below, the dam shafts were dug at a 55° incline to ensure a smooth flow of water to the four generators below in their huge machine room. It is that scale of construction which most impresses.

Three contractors took on the project: one for the aqueducts, one for the tunnelling and one for the fitting out. Each brought in gangs of workers from around the UK, totalling 1,300 men at its peak, accommodated in temporary camps that promptly became rife with drinking and gambling as the self-styled "Tunnel Tigers" relaxed in the way unique to young men whose employment involves considerable risk to limb and life.

A total of 36 men died in all, 15 while underground digging out the cavern and the rest in the construction of the tunnels and network of aqueducts feeding the upper loch.

There are 2.7 miles (4.5km) of aqueduct and more than 8.6 miles (14km) of tunnels catching rainwater from the surrounding hills. That rainwater took nine months to fill the reservoir and still contributes about 10 per cent of the power generated.

Having driven the kilometre into the mountain, visitors leave the bus and climb a short flight of steps to a sloping path past the fire system - where 20,000 gallons of water sit, just in case they're ever needed. Our guide, the slightly over-enthused Ian, tells us that the system is tested twice a week, but has never been used.

From there we're led past tropical plants, carefully placed to emphasise the heat - that far underground it remains a steady 18°C - and some of the tools used to dig out the caverns.

Which brings us to the final cavern, the thing we're here to see. Viewed from above it's a little difficult to fathom the scale of the space, and a good deal of it is held empty against the necessary removal of the turbines for servicing (something which happens every three years, with a complete refit every 15).

The 15 men who died underground are commemorated in a carved tribute affixed to the side of the machine hall. Visitors aren't allowed in the machine hall itself, we just look down from a high viewing gallery at one end, and photographs are forbidden for fear terrorists could make use of them, so you'll have to take our word for it that it's bloody big in there.

A good deal of the time the turbines sit idle, but when power is demanded they can be spun up in less than two minutes, under a minute if the pony (starter) motor is already spinning.

As we return Ian tells us of the "Tigers" and the life they led, and that one of the deaths wasn't the accident it appeared to be: the chap who kept the gambling book managed to get himself crushed under a truck in suspicious circumstances.

Certainly they were hard men, and the lack of health and safety shortened the life of many more than the 36 it killed as the (now) traditional Irish Crooked Jack reminds us.

But at least they got paid, unlike the prisoners of war who worked on the Loch Sloy (non-reversible) hydroelectric scheme a decade earlier.

One tends to think of hydroelectric power as a modern conceit, when in fact Cruachan will soon be up for its Golden Jubilee - Ian is even trying to get some of the Tunnel Tigers back on site this October to record their thoughts ahead of the 2015 anniversary.

Back in the visitors' centre there are buttons to push and panels to read, courtesy of Scottish Power. Visitors, or their children, can turn a clock to see when power is used and read all about how Scottish Power will supply it - they even have one of their Smart Meters on display.

Having said that, the exhibition, and accompanying video, won't entertain for very long, and while the trip into the mountain is impressively brought alive by Ian's commentary, it lasts only half an hour.

A hike up to the dam isn't difficult, though you cannot set out from the visitors' centre (a short drive is needed) and the climb requires stout shoes and a tolerance for bogs. Walk Highlands has an excellent guide.

But for the lazy, or offspring-encumbered, the Cruachan power station is more of a marvellous place to stop for a long lunch than a destination in itself. Makes for a very interesting lunch though, and the food isn't bad either.

GPS
56.395284,-5.11591

Post code
PA33 1AN

Getting there
By car: Cruachan Visitor Centre is on the north bank of Loch Awe, 19 miles east of Oban on the A85. By train: to Falls of Cruachan station 200 metres away, with services between Glasgow and Oban.

Entry
Admission to the exhibition is free. Guided tours are £7 for adults, senior citizens/ students: £6, children: six - 16 years £2.50, under six years are free.
Opening hours: April - October: 9:30am – 4.45pm, 7 days per week. November, December, February and March: 10am–3.45pm, Monday to Friday only. Closed in January. Bookings for tours strongly advised. The train station - charmingly named Falls of Cruachan - might be occasionally closed for engineering or maintenance, so call ahead if you're travelling by rail.

Online resources
www.visitcruachan.co.uk

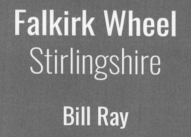

Falkirk Wheel
Stirlingshire

Bill Ray

 GEEK'S
GUIDE
TO BRITAIN

Meet the world's one-of-a-kind ENORMO barge-bowling bridge of Falkirk

When is a wheel not a wheel? When it's a lift

Meet the world's one-of-a-kind ENORMO barge-bowling bridge of Falkirk
When is a wheel not a wheel? When it's a lift

Proving it's not just the Victorians who can make huge structures in steel, the Falkirk Wheel can lift six canal boats 25 metres in one go, moving them from one waterway to another.

The Forth & Clyde Canal, running across central Scotland, used to be connected to the Union Canal, linking Glasgow to Edinburgh via a stairway of 11 locks. That stairway was closed up and filled in back in 1938. A millennium project to reconnect the canals needed something spectacular to go in their place, and this arrived in 2002 in the form of the Falkirk Wheel.

The wheel is huge (114.8ft or 35m across), though cunningly concealed from the car park so it emerges to dominate the landscape as one approaches on foot. The steel and concrete structure contains 15,000 hand-tightened bolts and one can't help but be reminded of some Victorian flight of fancy as it slowly revolves to deliver the 300-ton (304,814kg), perfectly balanced, gondolas.

The wheel can lift six boats at a time, consuming only 1.5 kilowatt-hours - enough to boil six to eight kettles as we're repeatedly reminded during our tour. The boats (and the water in which they sit) rise 82ft (25m) to the Union Canal, while the wheel lowers an equally-heavy load on the other side for balance. The balance is perfect as boats displace their weight in water while interlocking cogs keep the gondolas horizontal throughout.

It takes a little over five minutes for a full rotation, and the direction is changed every few days to keep the wear and tear evenly spread, though a good deal of the traffic is the tourist tour which goes up and down every couple of hours.

The Forth & Clyde Canal was opened in 1790 to provide a coast-to-coast (Firth to Firth) route as a shortcut for seagoing vessels as well as intra-Scottish trade. It was bankrolled by cash borrowed from the government, but it made money on tolls and taxes.

The Union Canal came 30 years later and spurred off from the Forth & Clyde to link up with Edinburgh, connected by the aforementioned stairway of 11 locks. It, too, was profitable, carrying horse-powered cargo and travellers on steam-driven "swifts" that had a projecting scythe to slice through row ropes of cargo craft too slow to move aside. It linked Glasgow to Edinburgh in less than seven hours. But the railways put paid to their profitability, cutting journey time and cost.

Both canals fell into disuse: the last commercial boats climbed the staircase in 1908, though the locks weren't filled in until 30 years later. In 1963 came the final indignity - the A80 was simply built across the Forth & Clyde Canal rather than over a bridge, as no one wanted canals any more.

But British canals had already started a rebirth as tourist destinations and sites for leisure activities. The millennium engendered an optimism ready to embrace Big Engineering, and the National Lottery was looking for showpiece projects to fund. So, in 1994, the Millennium Link was announced. The plan was to reopen both canals, and put something significant between them.

Suggestions were solicited, and the Falkirk Wheel (which is apparently based on the shape of a traditional two-headed axe) was the winning entry, not least because it looks so damned dramatic.

The Millennium Link project cost a total of £85.5m, £32m of which came from the National Lottery by way of the Millennium Commission, the rest coming from British Waterways and various local authorities along the route. £17.5m of that was spent on the Falkirk Wheel as a centrepiece to the project.

Principal architect Tony Kettle apparently built the whole thing out of Lego before selling the idea to the Commission, and it's easy to imagine how it would have looked in model form as the full-sized object defies scale until one can reach out and touch it.

Which is quite easily done even without taking the half-hour tourist trip. Adjacent to the wheel is a visitors' centre, which used to contain local history and information about how the mechanism works. These days that's reduced to a few wall hangings with space given over for the extended shop selling the usual gumble - but step outside and one is confronted by the reality of Big Engineering in action.

The tourist boat will take you for a half-hour trip up and down, but it's only a 10-minute walk to the Union Canal where you can walk through the last canal tunnel cut in Britain to the two traditional locks that raise boats the remaining 36ft (11m) The aqueduct leading to the upper end of the wheel is out of bounds, but the views are still pretty spectacular.

Sadly one can't get inside any part of the wheel, though engineering teams do venture into the central axle to grease the bearings every now and then.

Strange as it sounds not everyone is interested in watching massive machines turning all day. Children may be sold in a single turn (which can be guaranteed thanks to the regularly running tourist boat) but won't be distracted for more than a moment by the displays inside.

Thankfully there's a decent playground outside, and an amazing water park where the young 'uns can open and close valves, jump on pressure pumps and spin enormous wheels to carry water up and down slopes. There's even a child-powered Archimedes Screw to show off what's possible.

The water system is all integrated, so works best when there are children (and adults) all over it. There's also a second water park higher on the slope, though during our visit that wasn't in use, ironically because of heavy rain.

In good weather the wheel and surrounding area are spectacular, and there's plenty to see if the water park and wheel aren't enough. Rough Castle Fort is walking distance away, along with the Antonine Wall that runs above the newly cut tunnel, and the really bored can climb into a giant plastic ball and roll around in the docks for a bit, for a reasonable fee.

We expected to spend an hour or two visiting the Falkirk Wheel, just to see the engineering and take a boat trip to the top. We ended up spending an entire day walking around the area and working out how to feed water through the various channels in the park.

The boat trip isn't necessary, and the day is weather dependent, but when it comes to modern Big Engineering there's not much that can compare with the Falkirk Wheel.

GPS
56.000522, -3.841559

Post code
FK1 4RS

Getting there
By car from Edinburgh: take the M9 west for Stirling, exit at junction eight, follow signs for The Falkirk Wheel. From Glasgow: from the M80/A80, follow signs for Falkirk and then signs for The Falkirk Wheel. For more details, and for train and bus information visit the Falkirk Wheel web site's getting-here section.

Entry
Admission is free and parking on site costs £2 for the day. Boat trips cost £8.95 per adult, £7.95 for concessions and £4.95 per child. Opening hours: The Falkirk Wheel visitor centre and cafe are open every day from 10am to 5.30pm. The boat trips run at various times; you are strongly advised to check the website before travelling.

Online resources
http://www.thefalkirkwheel.co.uk/

Bletchley Park
Milton Keynes

Gavin Clarke

Hut 1 an original wartime code breaking hut. Now used to display a collection of Diplomatic Wireless equipment

WIRELESS TELEGRAPHY STATION

GEEK'S GUIDE TO BRITAIN

Photo: Gavin Clarke

Bletchley rebooted: The crypto factory time remembered

High commands and dirty words in German – the story retold

The Battle of Britain: it was won by the RAF and pilots in Hurricanes and Spitfires assisted by a new-fangled invention called radar that gave the enemy's position away.

It was the first campaign of World War II fought entirely in the air and was waged by Germany's Air Force, the Luftwaffe, against the UK's Royal Air Force (RAF) during the summer and autumn of 1940.

But the bit about the radar is not the whole story. The RAF command actually already knew the Luftwaffe's plans before their pilots took off from France during those long days of summer and autumn.

That's because the encrypted communications used by the Luftwaffe – thousands of messages about flight operations and targets – had been hacked by code-breakers of Bletchley Park, just outside Milton Keynes.

I learn this nugget about the Battle of Britain on a trip to Bletchley Park, armed with the Park's new self-guided tour - a ruggedised iPod on lanyard that comes free with the admission ticket. Drifting between the huts of Bletchley, where the code-breakers worked, I'm getting sucked in and becoming oblivious to my ever-slowing footsteps.

The iPod guide continues: working on other enemy communications, Bletchley Park's code-smashers decrypted reports that Hitler's prized battleship, the Bismarck, had asked for navigational charts... so that Britain could send out a pair of Supermarine Spitfires to sink it.

The code-breakers also played a crucial role in the June 1944 D-Day landings in Normandy. Bletchley's operators were among the first to learn of the German surrender and of two massive nuclear blasts in the Japanese cities of Hiroshima and Nagasaki that finally brought the war to an official end.

All this and more was only made possible by the fact Bletchley was a massive operation: between 9,000 and 12,000 dedicated staff (numbers vary) working intensely in shifts around the clock cracking hundreds of thousands of encrypted Axis military signals.

Two-thirds of staff were women, three of the staff were chess champions – recruited for their unique problem-solving abilities – and one Bletchley Park-er was Alan Turing, the father of modern computer science. Slaving in the huts I now pass, their work was hot in summer, cold in winter, grindingly repetitive all year 'round, and coders burned out.

Bletchley also saw the first computers ever used to hack crypto, called the Tunny and Colossus. The Colossus machines read 5,000 characters a second; with 10 Colossi operated by 500 staff they broke 63 million characters of "high-grade" German communications.

This story has been hidden from history. That's thanks to the war being a narrative shaped by gripping tales of the clash of men, the ripping of bullets and the sinking of steel. It's due, too, to the fact Bletchley was smothered into silence by the Official Secrets Act during and after the war. This place was so secret that pieces of paper stuffed into the cracks in huts' walls by those working inside, to keep out the cold winter winds, had to be removed after 1945 so that not one trace of Bletchley's wartime activities might be discovered.

This story is packaged in the self-guided iPod tour that comes with the admission ticket. Seven hundred iPods are in stock, paid for by the Bletchley Park Trust and supported by £4.6m in Lottery Fund cash. You can also download the guide from the iPhones App Store before your visit. The cash was also used on major renovations and work that tackled the neglected code-breaking huts and opening of a purpose-built visitors' centre opened in 2014.

There are two streams to the tour – one for adults and one for kids – which are presented differently. Adults get the Jeremy-Vine like Jonathan Foyle and kids, a redhead Women's Royal Navy Service (WREN) officer named "Dorothy". Foyle bestrides Bletchley while Dorothy operates behind a desk armed with blackboard, in-tray and glint in her eye. She is filmed in a scratchy, war-era cine-camera style.

Foyle packs in the facts and breaks out the veterans along with pertinent B&W clips from the war. Dorothy keeps the history bite-sized, colourful and interactive for the young 'uns.

You can tap through bios on code-breakers, get explanations of things like encryption and how the German cypher machines worked, and there are also quizzes and code-breaking challenges on schoolboy staples like Morse code.

The first challenge, though, is which tour to take: adults or kids? I mix and match, in case I miss something.

I begin at Bletchley Park's Victorian mansion, where British wartime code-breaking began. The 19th century pile and its grounds were bought by the government in May 1938 to serve as a base for the Government Code and Cypher School (GC&CS) - that became GCHQ - in the event of a future war. When that war came in September 1939 the operation was small, with just 200 staff and catering courtesy of chiefs from London's Savoy Hotel.

We're introduced to the first of the Germans' fiendish encryption devices: Enigma actually dated from World War I and, before it was adopted by the German military, was used by banks to encrypt messages to help prevent fraud. Enigma is an electro-mechanical device in a wooden case with a keyboard and set of three to five rotors. It was the rotors that disguised a character's meaning using a list of settings approved in a codebook. Enigma could muster a possible 159 million, million, million settings.

I move out, to the rear of the mansion where there is a water tower and some red brick and whitewashed cottages. The tower briefly hosted a radio receiver but was closed, lest its radio antenna and signal draw attention to Bletchley.

Here I learn Bletchley processed up to 20,000 messages each day from Enigma and later German machines. Messages were dispatched to London and PM Winston Churchill via motorcycle courier equipped with side arm. Later a teleprinter was used, attached to a phone line – but no leaky radio signals.

These cottages initially housed Turing and mathematician Peter Twinn, among others. Twinn cracked the first Enigma message for Bletchley after just four months, using brainpower and mathematical logic - the code-breaking machines Bletchley is known for had yet to arrive. His work had been informed by information given to Britain by Polish mathematicians who'd obtained Enigma machines and codes before the German army invaded their country. You'll find a book-shaped stone memorial to the Poles in this area.

On the adults' tour, we also learn of fellow mathematician and code-breaker Gordon Welchman. He headed up Hut 6, breaking the daily settings of the Enigma machines used by Hitler's air force during the Battle of Britain. Hut 6 sent its information to Hut 3 separated by a distance of just eight feet, where messages were translated, interpreted and dispatched. Messages were passed in Heath Robinson fashion between the huts using a wooden tray tugged along a runner via two pieces of string. The set-up was built by Bletchley's carpenters. Foyle interrupts these observations to say Hut 6 was "inundated" with German radio comms during the summer of 1940 - the start of the Battle of Britain.

It's here I get an insight into how the people breaking the codes worked. Each person was given just a fragment of each individual message – nobody ever got a complete cypher - to maintain total secrecy. "I was aware it was German codes, I was aware it was the Enigma machine, I was unaware of the content," Hut 6 code breaker Oliver Lawn says on the guide.

All well and good, but Bletchley was under enormous pressure to speed up the decoding. The German military used Enigmas on 100 different communications networks and - to complicate things - they changed the settings of the Enigma rotors each day. The German navy, meanwhile, had gone a step further by customising its own set of Enigmas with the addition of extra rotors and an additional set of codebooks.

The answer was Bletchley's first code-breaking machine, the Bombe, an electro-mechanical device designed by Turing and Welchman. Actually, Turing wasn't quite the invincible genius received wisdom tells us he is: his first version of the Bombe didn't work properly when it arrived in March 1940 and it took Welchman fiddling with the wiring to get things going properly.

The Bombe looks like a telephone switchboard filled with 180 coloured drums. Each drum represented three Enigma machines. Two hundred Bombes were built but none remain – instead you can see a replica at Bletchley.

The Bombe worked by a process of elimination, searching for the daily Enigma settings by looking for common phrases. Its results were fed into a separate Typex machine – a kind of typewriter operated by a human who chewed through the Bombe's results to spit out the decoded message at the other end.

Common phrases were recorded on boards, written using children's coloured crayons that happened to be lying around at the time and that stuck – green for the army, red for the air force and blue for – yes - the navy.

The Bombe operators were all WRENs - they also operated the later Tunny and Colossi. WRENs connected plugs and wires to create a "spaghetti junction", then they simply had to wait for the process to stop running.

Turing, I learn, dedicated himself to cracking the German navy's particularly fiendish flavour of Enigmas from his office in Hut 8, which you can visit. Something was missing, though: those decoding the navy's Enigmas needed the code books. One code book was stolen in May 1941 but the German navy went and added yet another rotor, making the codes unreadable again.

History took a turn in February 1942 with the acquisition of an updated code book, and that's where the Bletchley kids' tour out-guns the adult version. There's a Commando-comic style animation telling how German U-boat 559 was intercepted and attacked by ships of the Royal Navy and how the code books for its Enigma were lifted without the German military ever finding out.

It's a story of luck, daring and heroism as we learn that two crew from one of the warships that captured the U-boat – Able Seaman Colin Grazier and Lieutenant Anthony Frasson from HMS Petard – went back into the sinking vessel for a second tranche of code books but they went down with the boat when it suddenly sank. The men earned posthumous George Crosses.

It's these individual tales that come through in the guide and tell a story beyond the headlines of Alan Turing and the Colossus.

It brings me on to the WRENs, who actually ran the code-breaking machines. The WRENs worked in extreme temperatures during summer and winter inside the wooden and then concrete huts. Their work was tiring with the shifts running for eight hours around the clock, seven days a week.

Bombe operator Ruth Bourne's shift-times were changed each week and this would screw up people's body clocks. WRENs lost it. Bourne herself went to the Bletchley sick bay one day complaining of feeling "not very well" before collapsing in tears. The doc's prescription: four days' sleep with a constant supply of jugs of water by her bed followed by two weeks' leave. "Some didn't recover and go back to work," Bourne reflects.

The Germans were efficient, but they also made errors. It was their mistakes that gave Bletchley Park's operators crucial breaks in understanding the encryption and messages, as a section called "Cilli" explains. The Germans frequently used the airwaves for dirty talk about their girlfriends, giving the women at Bletchley plenty of laughs and allowing the decoders to build up a library of recognisable – if dirty - words. It's believed Cilli was the name of a German soldier's girlfriend.

Germany's Italian allies were sloppy, too, typing out full words rather than disguising then - for example, "incrociatore" for cruiser. This caught the Italians out at Cape Matipan in March 1941, the first military victory credited to Bletchley Park. The Royal Navy sank three Italian heavy cruisers, two destroyers and crippled the Italian's flagship in an action that claimed more than 2,400 Italian sailors for three British lives.

But it was the downing of Hitler's naval pride, the Bismarck, that's the real breath-taker. The sinking of the Bismarck was a priority: a monster ship weighing 50,000 tons, it had sunk the Royal Navy's HMS Hood with the loss of 1,416 crew and just three survivors picked up.

The Bismarck was big enough to menace food and supply lines to Britain coming across the North Atlantic from then-neutral North America. Sinking the ship was important, not just for British morale but also for the armed forces' material chances of staying alive during those dark early days of the war.

Anchored in Norway, Bismarck had slipped out to attack Allied shipping on 18 May 1941. The Navy brass didn't believe Bletchley's initial intercept about the ship's movements but when Bletchley decoded a second message between the ship's operators and shore that revealed Bismarck's final destination as the French port of Brest, the Navy scrambled. Three British battleships and 14 aircraft pounded the Bismarck, sinking her on 26 and 27 May, 1941.

The key piece of information that Bletchley decoded? A Luftwaffe officer named Hans Gesserlick on shore had radioed the Bismarck to enquire about the health of a family member among the crew. In this communication the ship's operators told Gesserlick of the Bismarck's destination – Brest.

Bletchley even decoded the last message from the ship's captain - "ship unmanageable, shall fight to last shell, long live the Fürher". News of the sinking that lunchtime produced spontaneous cheering in Bletchley's crowded canteen (the now-disappeared Hut 2).

The guide moves me on. Bletchley is best known for the Tunny and Colossus, introduced because the Germans had upped the intelligence ante with the

Lorenz SZ42 cypher machine. Lorenz messages bested the Enigma by using 12 rotors, giving it a possible 1.6 billion billion possible start positions each day. The Lorenz was used for Hitler and his High Command.

The Tunny was designed using simple deduction and inspired genius by Bill Tutte and built by scientists at the forerunner of BT, the General Post Office. Tunny, though, could only process final decrypts. The job of working out the original rotor settings was done by hand and still took days.

Colossus was built to perform numerical analysis of messages and cut the job of working out the start position of those 12 rotors to hours. The secret to Colossus was Thermionic valves – 2,500 by the time of the second Colossus in 1944. Valves were the idea of GPO engineer Tommy Flowers, who'd seen the GPO use the valves in its first, modern digital phone exchanges. Between 15 and 20 Tunnys and 10 Colossi worked at Bletchley.

Colossus played a major role in the success of the Allied landings in June 1944 - the landings that paved the way to eventual victory. The Allies had been distributing false intelligence that the landings were to take place in Calais. Listening to the messages from the ambassadors of German ally Japan on troop movements and on defence plans for Northern France, Bletchley learned the German High Command had swallowed the Allied deception. With the bulk of Hilter's defensive forces concentrated in Calais, the Allies landed 233 miles (375km) south in Normandy.

The guide tells about Tunny and Colossus while on a trip around the lake at Bletchley Park. This is a bit confusing but is explained because the machines ran in the buildings that now comprise The National Museum of Computing History (TNMOC), a short walk from the Bletchley manor and huts. Also, they were in a hut pulled down years ago with its site now beneath a car park. You can see the rebuilt Tunny and Colossus at TNMOC.

The guide is winding up and I've ground to a halt by the lake.

Time for refreshments. There's a decent Bletchley Park café, called Hut 4, tucked in next to the manor house. Hut 4 has adopted the National Trust template for refreshing the general public: spacious and well-presented, it serves hot meals, lush cakes and muffins, delicious soups – I opt for the carrot and coriander – and ready-made sandwiches. There's not much food-wise around Bletchley, so Hut 4 more than takes up the slack.

The self-guided tour takes about an hour and a half. You can either combine it with a visit to TNMOC – where you'll see those Colossus and Tunny rebuilds – or rejoin the world back in Milton Keynes (the next train stop north) and head back to London Euston in less than an hour. You could also pop over to Oxford and Cambridge, where many of the brains for Bletchley, including Turing, were recruited at the start of the war.

If you want to linger in the area, there's plenty of places to stay, visit and shop in Milton Keynes, Oxford and Cambridge. If you want to stay local, though, there's the Bletchley Park B&B.

Bletchley has a challenge. Fans of British tech will likely feel they know about the Bletchley story. Everybody else will overlook Bletchley's role in World War II thanks to the legacy of the Official Secrets Act and that dominant narrative.

But the self-guided tour changes this. It sheds new light on familiar chapters in the war and the surprising role Bletchley Park played. Moreover, the guide helps put names and faces to the people behind the mighty Colossi – people without whom Bletchley couldn't have functioned as it did.

My advice: go to Bletchley and plug in.

GPS
51.997367,-0.742911

Postcode
MK3 6EB

Getting there
By train: between 30-50 minutes from London Euston to Bletchley. By car: between the A5 and A421, north of London.

Entry
Winter opening: 1 November to 28 February, 9.30am to 4.00pm.
Summer opening: 1 March to 31 October, 9.30am to 5.00pm.
Entrance fee: adults £16.75, children 12-16 £10, under-12s go free, family tickets £38.50.
Concessions available.

Visitors to Bletchley Park can visit the Tunny and Colossus at TNMOC. Charges are £3 for the Tunny and Colossus galleries and £7.50 for the whole museum. The TNMOC Colossus and Tunny galleries are open daily; the rest of TNMOC is open every Thursday, Saturday and Sunday afternoon from 12pm.

Online resources
www.bletchleypark.org.uk

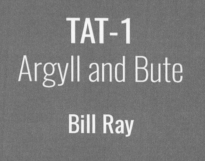

TAT-1
Argyll and Bute

Bill Ray

GEEK'S
GUIDE
TO BRITAIN

Photo: Bill Ray

TAT-1: Call the cable guy, all I see is a beautiful beach

57 years on, Reg man visits scene of first transatlantic voice call

A cabled telegram first crossed the Atlantic in 1858, but it took almost a century for voice calls to follow, being carried by the TAT-1 Cable which landed at Oban in Scotland, where we went along to see it.

Back in 1955 a phone call to Canada or the United States would require booking several hours in advance while the various radio links required were established – assuming atmospheric conditions allowed the connection to work at all. But on 25 September 1956, the first voice call crossed the pond from Newfoundland in Canada to Oban in Scotland, landing just here:

The cable carried 35 simultaneous calls, and 22 telegraph lines (squeezed into a 36th voice line), bringing down the cost of calling America to a pound a minute (bought in three-minute chunks) which would be worth about £20 now and compares well to BT's current rate of 45 pence to call the US.

But TAT-1, as the cable was known, didn't just carry public phone calls, it was also used to send the Queen's Christmas message to the Commonwealth – live - and was a vital segment of the Moscow-Washington hotline, which is why the 100 or so Post Office workers had to sign the Official Secrets Act.

Visiting the site of the cable landing isn't trivial. The bay is on the Gallanach Estate, about three miles south of Oban on a road which goes nowhere else. The cable's concrete housing vanishes entirely at high tide, but we dropped the MacDougalls an email and they were kind enough to let us look around at the point where so many historical phone calls crossed the Atlantic.

The concrete housing stretches several metres into the sea, and is wide enough to walk on, if a little slippery. There's no evidence of the cable itself, that's long gone, but turning back up the beach the termination building is still standing.

That building was where the cable connected to the rest of the phone network, continuing down to London as well as onwards to Moscow. That leader-to-leader telex link ran (and still runs, though not using telex and not over TAT-1) from the White House to the Kremlin and was designed to avoid the delays in communication that almost destroyed the world during the Cuban Missile Crisis.

The cable was switched off in 1978, but BT had workers there for another couple of years decommissioning the place. When they finally left, the estate owner bought back the land along with the building on it.

The building itself is quite dull and considered unsafe, though it's been explored on the Derelict Places site. Mrs MacDougall would like to see it turned into a house, and has clearly given the matter some thought, but current plans extend only to some sort of commemorative plaque recognising its place in history and as an IEEE Milestone.

TAT-1's terminal building, now considered unsafe
Photo: Bill Ray

To see actual cable, one needs to drop into Oban War and Peace Museum in the town centre, where a chunk of it proudly hangs beside the door along with some photographs and background on the project.

It's here we learn that £12.5m was spent on the pair of cables, which were funded by the Canadian Overseas Telecommunications Corporation, the

American Telegraph and Telephone Company (AT&T) and the UK Post Office, and that the first year saw 300,000 calls routed across the Atlantic.

The remains of TAT-1's concrete casing disappears at high tide
Photo: Bill Ray

The cable isn't central to the museum, which comprises a collection of artefacts with local connections, but there are some photographs of the workers pulling lengths of cable, and some history around the project.

Proper geeks will also be interested to see photographs of the listening station at Pennyfuir, where submarine transmissions would be intercepted and transcribed before being passed onto Bletchley Park for decoding.

Canadian broadcaster CBC also has some archive material on the cable, including a recording of the first call, between her Maj and the Canadian PM, and a contemporary documentary that includes a delightful conversation between the TV presenter and the then Mrs MacDougall – grandmother to the current estate owner.

It's hard to describe TAT-1 as a great day out for all the family. Get the timing wrong and the cable housing will be beneath the waves, and the museum is fun but won't justify the hundred-mile drive over the mountains - and that's starting from Glasgow!

Which is a shame as it's a real piece of British technical history, connecting the Commonwealth and ensuring that two world powers could threaten each other with alacrity before they started lobbing bombs.

The museum is free (donations welcome) so anyone travelling up the west coast of Scotland should drop by and if the weather's good and arrangements allow then the cable itself is well worth a visit, if only for the views.

GPS
Gallanach Estate
56.377222, -5.518265

Post code
PA34 4QL

Getting there:
A816/Soroba Road to Oban, then Gallanach Road to Gallanach Estate.

Entry
Gallanach Estate: enquiries to enquiries@gallanachestate.co.uk

GPS
Museum: Oban War & Peace Museum
56.415863, -5.473697

Post Code
PA34 5PX

Getting there:
A816/Soroba Road to Oban then via A85/Oban one-way system

Entry:
March, April, November: 10.00 to 16.00 daily including Sunday
May to October: 10.00 to 18.00 Monday to Saturday 10.00 to 16.00 Sunday
August: 19.00 to 21.00 Wednesday and Thursday only
December-February: Closed

Online resources
http://www.gallanachestate.co.uk/
http://www.obanmuseum.org.uk

The National Archives
Surrey

Joe Fay

How the UK's national memory lives in a ROBOT in Kew

El Reg visits the National Archives

The UK's National Archives in Kew have enough gems and hidden secrets to keep Indiana Jones or Robert Langdon in sequels for the next couple of centuries, with everything from the Domesday Book to the UK's official UFO records stocked away safely in its sanctum.

But for the swashbuckling archaeological hero of the future, whips, guns, and medieval symbolism will not be enough to unlock all of Kew's secrets. They will also need the ability to manipulate a tape library and emulate long-dead file formats.

That's because over the next couple of decades, the expansion of the UK's official national memory will no longer consist of handwritten vellum-based documents and lovingly typed Cabinet meeting minutes in buff-coloured folders. Rather, with government business increasingly being conducted electronically, the National Archives will also expand virtually, one cartridge at a time.

As the national memory of Britain, the National Archives is a comparatively recent invention. For centuries, official documents - crucially the statutes passed by Parliament and the judicial decisions that defined the UK's common law - were dispersed across bundles and trunks at sites including the Tower of London and the Palace of Westminster. Other key documents were in private hands.

Things became more systematic with the creation of the Public Records Office in the early 19th century. This was long headquartered in a soaring

Victorian Gothic building on London's Chancery Lane, though procedures were occasionally subject to the whim of individual "keepers".

The Grigg report of the 1950s laid down a new mission and methodology for choosing which documents should be preserved, including the 30-year rule. This new, modern approach to document-keeping clearly required a new, modern building for the documents.

The Ministry of Works, in its wisdom, chose a site in Kew: a World War I era hospital, which already housed the government's National Savings and Investments operation. The deeds of the historic few won out over the chances of riches for the modern hoi polloi, and ERNIE (Electronic Random Number Indicator Equipment - the machine that generates the winning Bond numbers each month) and the National Savings Institute staff were shunted off to Blackpool. The new PRO building was opened in 1977.

Kew gained The National Archives moniker in 2003 after the PRO was merged with other record-keeping organisations including the Historical Manuscripts Commission. The current site comprises the original PRO building, a fine example of 1970s municipal brutalism designed by the Ministry of Public Works, and a newer, lighter annexe.

The original building is saved from looking like a 1980s dole office or Job Centre by being skinned in light-coloured concrete, rather than the shit-coloured pebble-dash of so many of its contemporary government buildings. It is linked to the new building by a light-filled atrium/reception. With the enormous water feature out front and the leafy riverside location, it really is a nice place to visit. You're as likely to be run over by a bunch of over-excited schoolkids as hordes of tweed-encased researchers.

Despite the name change, the operative word is still "public". Anyone can walk into the lobby, veer left and hit the small museum covering some of the key items in the collection, including the Domesday Book, or head upstairs to the public reading rooms, where you can consult records online or on microfiche. Register for a "readers' ticket" and you can request original documents.

Beyond the museum is the inevitable bookshop and a canteen, also public. When we visited there was chocolate bread-and-butter pudding on the menu, and the BBC's historian du jour, Lucy Worsley, signing books in the bookshop. You might not be so lucky when you visit. Sometimes it's rhubarb crumble.

After tea in the canteen with CIO David Thomas, we were taken into the newer wing, the domain of the archivists, web and database developers, historians and restorers who maintain the collection, and ensure that it is available to the people who pay for it - ie, you.

The new wing has a long, light-filled atrium which is lined with framed photographs. On closer inspection these prove to be the staff's own work: holiday landscapes, wildlife, still lifes. Dotted amongst these are also lots of posters for yoga and meditation classes. They must work. The people we met there seemed engaged in their work, but not unduly stressed. The archive has been a thousand years in the making, so perhaps that gives you a slightly different perspective on time.

It possibly also helps that the site - or at least the repositories where the documents are kept - is literally bombproof. Fire safety is also paramount, with suppressant gas on tap rather than water. And, unsurprisingly, the site is built to withstand floods - reassuring given its Thames-side location.

As you approach the repositories themselves - the actual document storage areas - you are gently reminded that these are pencil-only areas. Got that? No pens, no food, no drink. No smoking, either? Need you ask.

As for the rooms themselves, don't be thinking *Raiders of the Lost Ark*. The repositories are large, though not cavernous: the ceilings need only be high enough to accommodate top shelves within arm's reach. Warning posters detail exactly how to protect both the nation's history and your back when handling the bigger box files. The repositories in the older part of the complex have narrow windows to afford the bookworms access to daylight, while ledges and skirting boards are brightly painted, all part of the old Ministry of Works strategy to keep the workforce happy. Temperature and humidity are carefully managed across the repositories, to keep mould and other threats at bay.

We saw a pile of blackened rolled-up manuscripts on a trolley, like props from a Harry Potterfilm, en route to or from some historical researcher. Picking a box at random off a shelf in one of the storage rooms, we found field survey books for a proposed early 20th century land tax. It never happened: World War I intervened, but the neat handwritten notes, still piled up in Kew, give a copperplate, ground-level snapshot of England just before that particular catastrophe.

Some plan drawers yielded a hand-drawn view of the 18th century harbour at Guadeloupe. This was in French: how did this French map come into British hands? Other drawers revealed sheet after sheet of tobacco and whisky advertising posters from the 19th century, a legacy of the Worshipful

Company of Stationers' erstwhile role in registering copyright.

Other shelves also hold regimental records, civil service papers, cabinet minutes, various PMs' correspondence, railway plans. Anything that is needed to track the progress and development of a country and much more besides.

Of course, you need some way of navigating this pile of history. Until the mid-1990s, this was via the vast paper-based catalogue. Even with this, tracking a soldier's career via his paybooks and regimental records, or tracking the policy turns that drew the UK into World War I meant a researcher needed to know, almost feel, their way around the collection - even if only PRO employees were allowed to enter the repositories to retrieve the documents.

If only there was a machine that could pinpoint exactly the document you need and tell you where it is. Or even deliver you a copy instantly. Even faster than the microfiche machines in the reading rooms...

When the PRO opened, back in the 1970s, it had one computer: a DEC-based docket ordering system used to manage requests to retrieve an item from the archive.

As Thomas, a 40-year veteran of the PRO, explains in the mid-1980s, a few PCs started to appear on the desks of key members of staff. However, these were not networked until some time in the mid-1990s. Around the same time, the PRO took its first steps onto the web - though there is no evidence for that, as that first site was not actually archived.

If mid-'90s surfers found this system less than interactive, things were not much better for the PRO staff administering the site. Thomas says the process for updating the site involved sending a floppy disk to the government's Central Computer and Telecommunications Agency in Norwich, once a month.

The web operation was brought in-house in 1996 - though it has fluctuated between in-house and contracted out ever since.

The catalogue itself began to move online in 1998, the first national archive in the world to do so. Someone presumably had to key it in - a gargantuan task. The catalogue currently stands at around 21 million entries.

The closest thing to a big bang for the archive was the release of the 1901 census online in 2002.

The names on this census were people within living memory of 21st century Britons with access to computers and the net. The stage was set for a massive explosion in interest in genealogy - or a complete disaster. In the event it was both, with Thomas confirming the system - built by sometime defence contractor Qinetiq - was completely "overwhelmed" initially as Britons opened their shiny laptops, fired up their new internet connections, and found out just how grindingly poor their great, great grandparents were.

It got over it though. Last year, the website clocked 13 million visits from 230 countries. The UK accounted for 63.6 per cent. Interestingly, "wills" was consistently the top search term last year, except for one month when it was ousted by UFO.

Surprisingly perhaps, the website, and in fact all the National Archive's IT, is handled on-site. There are 210 servers, all Xeon-based HPs. A dozen of these are used to host a further 150 virtual servers. The site currently has 316TB of storage on tap.

The catalogue, too, is an in-house development. The "new" catalogue, Discovery, was launched in 2011. It is based on Mongo DB, and subject to regular updates. At just over 100TB when first deployed in 2011, it is expected to run into PBs within the next few years.

The archive itself has recently been subjected to a tsunami of data. Firstly, you might not have noticed, but in 2013 the UK government shifted from the Grigg Report's 30-year rule for moving documents from Whitehall closets to public archives, to a 20-year rule. Serving politicians and civil servants' early career screw-ups are therefore now likely to come into public view mid-career.

And the wave continues. For the more technically minded, the early 1980s also corresponds with the time when computing and electronic comms and electronic record keeping started to make its way into government. The assumption is that by 2025 pretty much everything that finds its way into the archive in future will be "digital born" - though the National Archive expects some departments will still be sending paper down to Kew "for many years after that date".

This might sound like a recipe for a pretty seamless archiving process. You produce the definitive electronic version of a document, it is circulated, then in time finds its way to Kew and is preserved for posterity.

On the other hand, consider this. What word processor were you using 20 or 30 years ago? Where are the files you created with it? Have you still got the floppy disks it came on? Don't tell me you have files you created in Microsoft Works?

Scale that up across the sprawl that is central government, with its shifting departmental structures, erratic and siloed procurement strategies, and at times piecemeal upgrade programmes. Throw in the debate on politicians' and advisers' use of private PCs.

Suddenly you can see the prospect of a first world country that can no longer access, much less understand, its own historical documents.

To head off this nightmare, the archive has developed its own file format ID tool, Pronom. As Alex Green of the Archive's Digital Records Infrastructure team explains, they "point it at a collection and it IDs the file formats". Except when it doesn't. When the archive took delivery of the records from the London Organising Committee of the Olympic and Paralympic Games (LOCOG) after the Olympic torch was snuffed out, it threw up lots of formats that weren't recognised. Had the long-feared cyber attack on the London Olympics come to pass, albeit after the closing ceremony? The answer was a lot more prosaic. It turns out that LOCOG had tended to work on Macs, which as Green gently puts it, "is not usual in government".

At the same time, the team has collaborated with Tessella to develop a tool called Safety Deposit Box, which it describes as "a risk-based system to identify formats in danger of becoming obsolescent".

Green says: "We make sure everything we get is on a hard drive. It's backed up in the dark archive [more on that later]... you can't put anything in there where we don't know what it is. It's very controlled." Incoming files are integrity-checked.

That takes care of the country's internal documents - the minutes, the policy papers, the grand plans, and the grubby excuses that come in their wake.

But this is just the internal information from the government. And the Armed Forces. And assorted state agencies.

What about the stuff that business might call the customer or citizen-facing content? Yep, the National Archives has to look after that too, and it is now also the home of the UK Government Web Archive.

Bizarre as it may seem now, when UK.gov first dipped its toe into the internet 20 years ago, it didn't occur to many people that websites should be archived.

Some of the earliest UK government ventures on to the web are sadly lost to history. The earliest finds, dating back to 1997, actually came from the Internet Archive Project.

Now the archive strives to preserve the UK government's web presence for posterity: U-turns, right-turns and all. It uses a crawler to trawl the UK government's web estate, aiming to hit sites every six months. With the government looking to shutter many obscure or unloved sites, the pressure is on. The Web Archive currently stands at around 80TB, with the crawler pulling in 1.6TB a month. At time of writing, there are 3 billion urls in the archive, with 1 billion captured last year alone.

But does anyone really care? Seems like they do. Espley said the archive gets around 15 to 20 million page views a month. This often maps to current events - the assumption being that visitors are often cross checking current government positions/statements against previous positions. When we dropped in, "badgers" was a top search term - this was the same month the badger cull had kicked off.

As the NHS's care.data program grinds on, old NHS pages detailing the NPFIT will no doubt race up the rankings.

And as government continues to sprawl, no matter who is in power, so does the Web Archive's purview. Thus it will be extending its archiving activities to cover social media in a couple of months.

Between the Web Archive and the increasing amount of "digital born" internal government documents, it feels inevitable that the amount of data in the electronic archive will swiftly outstrip that from pre-digital days, if it hasn't already: no one has calculated exactly how much data a fully digitised version of everything in the Archives would require.

Still, storage companies in particular are regularly telling us more data is now created every couple of days than was created between the dawn of humanity and 2003. If that data fits the mission of the National Archives, then it has to be preserved... somewhere.

That somewhere is well above the waterline, just off one of the repositories, and is known as both the Dark Archive and the Robot Room. The Robot in question is a Sun StorageTek SL3000 tape library. One half runs LTO6, says Thomas, the other half is Sun's own tape format. The tapes themselves are standard 6.25TB cassettes. It's clearly an archive. The "Dark" bit of Dark Archive refers to the fact that when no one is in the room, the lights are off, rather than any suggestion that this is the "real" archive of the illuminati who really run the UK.

As we said earlier, newer collections generally arrive in a digital format and go straight into the Dark Archive. If you're wondering what key "historical" events we're talking about, Thomas quickly reels off the Hillsborough Inquiry, The Leveson Inquiry, the Olympic Games and the records for the latest Census.

The tape library has a theoretical maximum of 13PB, and the Dark Archive is expected to hit 6PB by 2020. By then around 0.63PB of data will be added to the archive every year.

Raider of the lost archive – the National Archive's dark storage
Photo: Joe Fay

Tape is not perhaps the sexiest of storage media - no helium, little in the way of nanometer scale technology beyond the media itself. But, as Thomas points out, it is a known technology, with us since the 1930s, and cheap - both in cost and environmentally. The tape vendors say it has a 30-year life cycle. While it remains to be seen whether that pans out, the team at Kew tests its existing tapes regularly, we're assured.

"This is the future of web archiving," says Thomas, picking up a tape, adding, "at the moment."

As an aside, the and 800-year-old Magna Carta are both written on sheepskin and are still readable to anyone with a passing familiarity with Latin and the urge to pop down to the museum at Kew. HP and Sun have plenty to prove. So, what of those shelves of files, books, parchment and the rest? Shouldn't the National Archives simply digitise the lot, then leave the originals mouldering in a vast annexe to a small room full of tapes?

Unlikely. Before a collection can be digitised, and therefore served up to the website and committed to tape, it has to be prepared for imaging. This is a conservation job in itself. Capturing the image is just part of the process - you then have to produce the appropriate files, transcribe them and prepare them for publication.

Just imaging a small collection - say 5,000 images - takes about four weeks. Larger collections take months, or even years. It's a job for the patient.

So, if the rest of the building felt generally focused and calm, the National Archives' conservation department takes this to another level. It's on the ground floor, and when you walk in it's like stepping back into the school woodwork room - a large space filled with daylight, with rows of large work tables, and aromas of oil and glue. Some of the tools – enormous cast iron presses, and vicious-looking guillotines – look almost as old as the documents.

It's easy to visualise committed conservators painstakingly repairing precious manuscripts, or rebinding ancient books using artisanal linen and animal-based glue.

But the head of conservation, Juergen Vervoorst, talks as much about the importance of overall "environment" and the "performance of the building". Which makes sense. Most of the collection is unlikely to be touched from one end of the year to another. Once you head off the environmental threats - heat, light, moisture, critters - the biggest threat is going to be handling.

At least that's the case with the older materials, whose characteristics are reasonably well known.

"The British government always paid attention to high quality paper. We don't really have a massive problem," says Vervoorst.

However, the newer materials - all those laminates, printer papers, etc, that crept into offices from the 1980s onwards - have "completely different ageing characteristics... their life expectancy is probably much shorter". Similarly, as photographic materials became more prevalent, "there [are] more problems to be expected".

Asked what particular items send a shiver up his spine, Vervoorst reels off the "treasures" housed at Kew. Domesday, not one but two copies of Magna Carta, Shakespeare's portfolios, Jane Austen's diary, Henry VIII's divorce papers from Anne Boleyn.

But for sheer spine-tingling magic, he picks out Kew's copy of The Treaty of Versailles, which officially tied up World War I, and set the stage for World War II.

Not because of what it was, but for what it could have been: "History could have been so different with a different treaty in 1919."

It's easy to imagine Vervoorst, indeed any historian, pondering the signatures of the peace treaty between Germany and the Allied Powers, contemplating how they got there and imagining how things might have been different.

GPS
51.481741, -0.279669

Post code
TW9 4DU

Getting there
Take the overground train or tube to Kew Gardens. The R68 bus terminates outside. By car, set your satnav for TW9 4DU. Parking space is limited and allocated on a first come, first served basis.

Entry
The National Archive is open from 9am to 5pm on Wednesdays, Fridays and Saturdays. On Tuesdays and Thursdays it's open until 7pm. It is closed Sunday and Monday.

Online resources
www.nationalarchives.gov.uk/visit/

de Havilland Museum
Hertfordshire

Ed Moore

Photo: Ed Moore

Mosquitoes, Comets and Vampires: The de Havilland Museum

When the British aerospace industry was more than just British Aerospace

Approaching the museum down a bumpy single track road you start wondering if any of this makes sense. Why is this museum in the middle of nowhere? Why are the opening hours so peculiar? Why are there bits of aircraft lying around? Why does it have two different names?

All becomes apparent in due course, in the process revealing the fascinating stories of not only a great engineering company and a special aeroplane but also how a group of enthusiasts built a museum from scratch.

That museum – the de Havilland Museum near St Albans – celebrates the story of the de Havilland Aircraft Company and one aircraft in particular, the twin-engined DH.98 Mosquito of World War II. The Mosquito airframe came here first, hence why all the signs on the surrounding roads point to the "Mosquito Museum". But the site expanded to take on the whole history of the de Havilland Company and so was renamed to reflect the broader remit.

Every item in the museum has a link to the company itself but also provides lessons on the broader British aircraft industry – and, if you look for it, the ups and downs of capitalism. It interplays with technology too. If you understand the company, the development history of the aeroplanes you see at the museum will make more sense, so on with the story...

The story of de Havilland is also that of its founder and namesake Geoffrey de Havilland. An entrepreneur in the classic mould, he worked in the aeronautics industry for almost his whole life, not only designing revolutionary aircraft but also building the companies to manufacture and sell them. After engineering school – just like any modern-day startup –

Geoffrey borrowed money from his grandfather to build his first aircraft in 1909.

Using an aero engine he also designed himself, the aircraft crashed on its first flight. Undaunted, he went on to build a second aeroplane with which he taught himself to fly and subsequently sold it to his new employer, the Royal Aircraft Factory. He was poached in early 1914 to become chief designer at Airco, a private aircraft manufacturer based in Hendon, north London. Throughout World War I Geoffrey designed successful aeroplanes for the Royal Flying Corps, from the DH.1 to the DH.9, which in its 9A variant went on to serve with the RAF for another two decades.

By 1918 Airco was the world's largest aircraft manufacturer – but the end of the war and the consequent drop in sales proved fatal to the company. Despite moving into passenger aeroplanes the company remained unprofitable. It was finally taken over by BSA, of small arms and motor vehicle fame, in 1920, but Airco's new parent company only wanted factory capacity for their growing car business. This proved the opportunity Geoffrey was waiting for: he bought out the aircraft assets and set up shop under his own name in Edgware, near to Hendon, and later moved to premises in Hatfield, just up the road from the present-day museum.

Initially de Havilland concentrated on the light aircraft market, producing a series of aircraft based on the Moth, an existing Airco design but using Geoffrey's own-designed Gipsy engines. Notable models included the first Moth, the DH.60 and the most famous of all Moths, the Tiger Moth, used widely to train military pilots well into World War II.

The basic plywood Moth design spawned many versions for specific purposes. A touring version, the DH.83 Fox Moth, had wings that folded back so you could tow it home easily. The larger DH.84 Dragon, a twin-engined development of the Fox Moth, was used for scheduled passenger and mail services, evolving into the iconic 1934 DH.89 Dragon Rapide. The most unusual was the Queen Bee: a Tiger Moth fitted with remote control equipment to serve as an anti-aircraft gunnery target. The museum has one – suggesting someone was not a terrific shot.

An important development of this period (but one which I can't help feeling was done just for marketing) was the DH.88 Comet. This was in response to the MacRobertson International Race from London to Melbourne announced in 1933. With no British aeroplane of the time being suitable, Geoffrey de Havilland announced he would build one. His final design (which won the race in a time of 71 hours) was a wooden box construction covered in plywood and fabric with tuned Gipsy engines. Lightweight and extremely streamlined for better performance, it would serve, along with the four-engined DH.91 Albatross airliner, as the forebear of the Mosquito. Having concentrated on building small, light aircraft, de Havilland was in danger of becoming simply a subcontractor as the clouds of war began gathering over Europe in the mid-1930s. One market that did interest the company, though, was that for a twin-engined bomber, called for by the Air Ministry in specification P.13/36. de Havilland started by reworking the Albatross using Rolls-Royce Merlin engines but it fell short of requirements, prompting a radical rethink.

While the need was set down for an armed bomber capable of defending itself, de Havilland preferred the idea of an unarmed bomber using just its speed to avoid the enemy. It would be fast, streamlined and – in what would later prove a useful step – would be made of wood.

The idea was taken to the Air Ministry who showed no interest. What to do? Like a true entrepreneur with a vision, Geoffrey de Havilland started work anyway, in October 1939. The design team, initially comprising eight people, was moved away from the main manufacturing plant in Hatfield to the secrecy of Salisbury Hall a short distance away - which is, of course, the site of the current museum.

de Havilland's designers worked in the main hall of the moated manor house while the prototype airframe was assembled in a small hangar alongside, disguised as a farm building. The design was radical. Built almost entirely of wood, it was structured as a single wing, to which the engines and fuselage were simply attached with just four bolts. The structure followed that of the Albatross, with a wooden structure glued and screwed together (using 30,000 screws per aircraft), covered in plywood and then fabric.

No rivets meant a very smooth skin and with no gun turrets – a standard feature of bombers back then – a streamlined shape. Two Merlin engines supplied the power and the whole prototype was designed and put together in just 11 months. When ready to fly the pieces of plane (now given the company designation DH.98) were put on lorries, shipped to Hatfield, assembled again and the maiden flight was made.

Although started under its own steam the project now had some official backing, initially from Air Marshal (later Air Chief Marshal) Sir Wilfrid Freeman, Air Member for Development and Production at the Air Ministry. Being made of wood it fulfilled a new requirement, B.1/40, for a fast long-range bomber-reconnaissance aeroplane made from "non-essential" materials: ie it wasn't metal, which was in short supply.

The new aircraft, named the Mosquito, easily surpassed expectations.

During acceptance trials it reached 392mph (630kph) and even outpaced a Spitfire in a head-to-head contest, leading to an initial order for 50 examples.

The sheer flexibility of the Mosquito airframe was its greatest strength. Built in two basic forms of fighter or bomber it performed a variety of tasks: night fighter; pathfinder; photo-reconnaissance; strategic bomber; sea patrol and fighter-bomber. Armament varied widely too: four .303" Browning machine guns and four 20mm Hispano cannon were the normal complement for a fighter variant, with hardpoints available for bombs, anti-ship torpedoes and rockets in later years. Even a bomb-bay-mounted 57mm anti-tank gun was installed on the FB.Mk XVIII.

A well-weathered de Havilland Sea Vixen
Photo: Ed Moore

The "Mossie" saw use throughout the war, with one of its most famous roles being in the Pathfinder squadrons. Here the Mosquito units led streams of four-engined heavy bombers to their targets by using the Oboe navigation system, which greatly increased the effectiveness of night bombing campaigns. Of higher profile was the strategic bombing of the Gestapo's Oslo headquarters and the Amiens prison raid; the approaches for these raids being made at just 60 feet (18m) above ground level for maximum surprise.

Arguably the finest aircraft of the war, the Mosquito's era ended as jet engines broke new performance records, but the company continued to forge ahead.

de Havilland entered the jet era in typical fashion by putting its broad range of aero-engineering skills straight to use. Not only did it make its own jet engines (the Halford H.1 being the first, used initially in the rival Gloster Meteor) but it produced complete military and commercial aircraft of often radical design, such as the tail-less, ill-fated DH.108 Swallow, all three examples of which were destroyed in fatal crashes. One such crash claimed the life of Geoffrey de Havilland Jr., son of the company's founding father, in 1946.

Operational roles started with the twin-boom DH.100 Vampire jet fighter and continued with the similarly equipped DH.110 Sea Vixen for carrier deployment with the Royal Navy's Fleet Air Arm. In the commercial field de Havilland was equally ambitious and with the DH.106 Comet launched the world's first commercial jet airliner in 1952. Early aircraft failures due to challenges previously never encountered by aircraft manufacturers led to extensive redesign work and slow sales, but despite rivals such as Boeing learning from de Havilland's problems and leaping ahead, the Comet astonishingly continued in service until 2011, in the form of the RAF Nimrod airborne early warning aircraft.

Despite other advanced work on Blue Streak ballistic missiles and even satellite launch rockets, de Havilland was unable to gain enough commercial contracts and in 1960 was taken over by Hawker Siddeley. The company's designs continued, with the DH.121 entering commercial service as the Hawker Siddeley Trident, but the iconic name eventually disappeared. Hawker Siddeley itself disappeared into British Aerospace in the 1977 nationalisation of the remains of the British aerospace industry. An era of British private aircraft companies, led by its most pioneering engineers, passed into the history books.

The museum itself is a delight and a wonderful example of what can be achieved by volunteer enthusiasts rather than government largesse.

Yes, it can appear ramshackle but that's part of the charm. It remains completely run by volunteers and without any government support the museum has added hangars and exhibition space as funds allow, and continues to restore and maintain the planes held there in full view of visitors. The volunteer ethos running through the museum also means more interaction than you would expect.

The team likes messing about with aeroplanes and so wants you, the visitor, to get as hands-on as possible too. If an airliner's door is open, poke your head in and have a look about. If a cockpit is open, jump in and feel for yourself what flying that aircraft must have been like.

The initial push to preserve and display de Havilland aircraft came from a Walter Goldsmith who bought Salisbury Hall after the war and realised the Mosquito had been designed there. Contacting the company's PR department, he found out the original prototype, serial number W4050, was still in Hatfield and needed a home, which he graciously offered. The Mossie arrived in 1959, making the de Havilland Museum the oldest aircraft museum in the country and unique in displaying a prototype on the original site where it was designed and built.

The museum is home to the largest collection of Mosquitos
Photo: Ed Moore

Over the years more aircraft arrived, always with an association with de Havilland or the site itself. Early pre-war exhibits include the Tiger Moth and the aforementioned Queen Bee, plus oddities such as a Cierva C.24 helicopter, for which de Havilland produced the airframe. The World War II part of the museum is all about the Mosquito and they have three examples, the world's largest group of the aircraft. Alongside the prototype are both fighter and bomber variants plus an extensive display of weaponry options, including the impressive 4,000lb blast bombs, cannon and machine guns.

They also have examples of the drop fuel tanks used to extend aircraft range, and even bulletproof windscreens! Another item of note from this period is a section of Handley Page Horsa fuselage, from a glider used to drop paratroopers behind enemy lines.

Aeroplanes from the post-war period are well represented and, being larger, can be mainly found outside. They include the Vampire and Sea Vixen military jets and examples of both the Comet and Trident airliners, plus light training aircraft such as the Chipmunk.

Alongside the planes are also displays on the company history and development of the jet engines from the later years. The museum is completed by - of course - the museum shop, for you to stock up on aircraft models, books and the necessary refreshments. You can still see the original hangar entrance set in concrete next to the hall.

Behind it are newer hangars housing the older airframes but the future will hopefully be built behind these; a new hangar is planned to move almost all the aeroplanes under cover and help preserve them for future visitors. Planning permission has been requested, now it's up to you. Go visit and help them raise the funds they need to build it.

Beyond this are places to reflect, and even entertain those in the family with less of an interest in this chapter of aviation: Willows Farm, which is good for smaller children who may not want to look round the museum, and Colney Fields Retail Park. Why they'd want to miss this gem, however, I can't imagine.

GPS
51.710943,-0.270534

Postcode
AL2 1BU

Getting there
The museum is located next to Salisbury Hall at junction 22 of the M25. NB: if you are travelling clockwise on the M25 (ie, from Heathrow, M1) you will need to cross back over the bridge on the M25.

The museum is signposted 'Mosquito Museum' from the London Colney roundabout and is on the B556 to South Mimms.

Entry
The museum is open from the first Sunday of March to the last Sunday of October. Opening times are eccentrically Tuesdays, Thursdays, Fridays and Saturdays, Sundays and Bank Holidays 10.30-5pm with last entry at 4pm.

The cost of entry is £8 for adults, £7 for senior citizens/students and £5 for children aged 5-16 (under 5s free). Family tickets are £23.00. Private tours and group booking by arrangement, phone for details. See the official website for more details.

Online resources
www.dehavillandmuseum.co.uk

Hursley Park
Hampshire

Joe Fay

IBM Hursley Park: where Big Blue buries the past, polishes family jewels

How the Internet of Things has deep roots in the English countryside

Would you like to work in a cross between Downton Abbey and Silicon Valley? For a small selection of IBMers, that's the only way to describe their working environment, although the place we're talking about is officially called Hursley Park.

You can get there by turning off the M3 and rattling through some pretty English village-hood before hitting Hursley, a high-end hamlet straddling the A3090. Cross over, skirting the stone bench built around a tree trunk, and you've entered the gateway to the Hursley Park estate, home to an IBM R&D lab since the late 1950s.

It was cold and grey the day we went. Chain link fences on either side of the road make it feel like you're entering some kind of government research facility. Think Baskerville in the BBC's 21st century take on Sherlock. However, this slightly forbidding entry quickly gives way to wide open green parkland with wooden paddock fencing.

A pheasant perched on a fence post looked completely unconcerned as we set course for the main house. While there are signs aplenty for the IBM tennis and cricket clubs, presumably there's no shooting club.

The estate itself has a chequered history, at one time belonging to Oliver Cromwell's son Richard; then the Heathcote family, who built the guts of the current house; the Baxendale family - owners of Pickfords; and then the Coopers, who massively extended the Heathcote's house.

So far so *Brideshead*. But things took a high-tech turn in the 1940s, when the house was requisitioned by the government and became a country hideout for Vickers Supermarine's design team, where they carried out refinements of the Spitfire and Hurricane, and laid the groundwork for the UK's post-war jets.

After the... let's say... consolidation of the British aerospace industry, an up-and-coming US technology firm called IBM moved into the building in the 1950s, initially using the house as a development lab, before buying the estate in full in the 1960s.

The site has been instrumental in the development of IBM's software technologies since the 1950s, as well as displays and disk-based storage, though those lines have now departed. It is still the home of development for CICS MQ Series technology. Or, put another way, the software that probably runs transactions on the mainframe underpinning your retail bank, and ensures the oil finds its way along the pipeline to your local petrol station.

Pulling up outside the house itself feels like the beginning of an intimate weekend in a country house hotel. Open fields to the left, woods to the front, imposing Queen Anne portico. Where are all the engineers, we wonder, before musing on whether we can expect an imposing yet slightly eccentric butler to announce our arrival.

We then realise we're at the wrong entrance. A walk around the side, past the old house's orangery/conservatory, brought us to the thoroughly modern plate-glass reception area, which fronts the vast complex of development labs.

We were picked up by our minder for the day, John from IBM's press operation, rather than a trusted family retainer, and taken into the main complex.

The wall immediately behind the lobby was lined with portraits. These were not of Hursley's previous inhabitants, but of the current inmates, complete with job titles like senior inventor.

Our first move was to walk back to the grand house, via a covered walkway which connected via the conservatory. En route, we passed a massive model of the site, which revealed just how much office and lab space had been plonked down in this quiet corner of Hampshire. How had IBM managed to get this all past the planners and into the middle of Jane Austen land? Mainly by building over the footprint of the massive hangars and drawing rooms that had been there previously, courtesy of Vickers - brownfield development, before the term was invented.

Into the main house and up to check in with John McLean, IBM vice president and lab director (McLean has since become IBM VP and chief technology officer for Europe). And then it was time to descend into the bowels of the house – to visit the museum... in an R&D centre.

But surely it would just be a collection of knick-knacks to amuse passing visitors? Shouldn't it be in reception?

Hardly. A visit to the basement of Hursley opens up an Aladdin's cave of kit that you've either heard of spoken in whispers, or, if you're old enough, will spark memories of long days spent hacking code, or perhaps just hacking recalcitrant IBM kit to bits.

Our host for the visit was curator Terry Muldoon. The ebullient IBM veteran is an enthusiastic pitchman for generations of Big Blue's kit, all the more so given that everything he shows us has been off the catalogue for years.

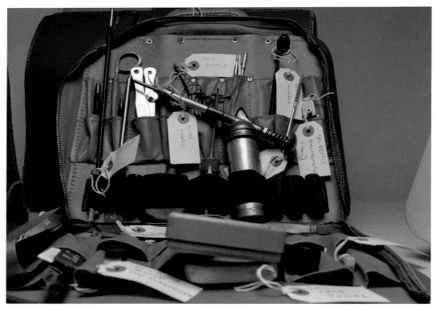

A mainframe repair kit
Photo: Joe Fay

The museum's story begins well before the birth of IBM as we know it. Muldoon shows off the original Hollerith product range - weighers, punch clocks and the like. This was IBM's bread and butter before it became the Computing Tabulating Recording Company - the firm's name before it rebranded again as International Business Machines in 1924.

Time flies, and before you know it you're looking at punch card machines, and remembering those two summers you spent working at a market research firm in the 1980s, where results were still processed on an armful of heavyweight paper. We see early circuit boards that look more like the innards of 1940s radiograms than a PC motherboard, complete with bulbous glass valves. There are plenty of typewriters, of course, to spark some deep-seated Mad Men-type fantasies.

A side room holds a collection of RS/6000 machines. Muldoon explains that much of the kit was collected after the fact - ex-marketing kit, for example - and that only recently has the firm actually thought to keep an archive of its wares. Why warehouse technology when you can sell it? In another room, Muldoon shows off what must be one of the last Token Ring networks running in the UK.

There is plenty of heavyweight veteran storage. Storage was one of the site's areas of expertise, and Hursley delivered many storage firsts. However, the estate was not the birthplace of the Winchester drive. Although the Ancient Capital of England is just up the road, the Winchester was so named because it had two storage modules of 30MB each, recalling the 3030 Winchester rifle cartridge. All the same, Muldoon has both the storage and the ammo versions on display.

Where the museum really springs into life – for us at least – is with the onset of the mainframe. One room is kitted out as a service room for a mainframe circa the 1960s. From the manuals detailing the software and innards of those early monsters, to a range of tools that would put even the most gadget crazy mechanic or surgeon to shame, it shows just what level of resource the early computing customers were prepared to shell out for to keep their machines – and companies – running.

We particularly liked the fact that the mainframe engineers were provided with a portable toolkit which fitted into a portmanteau, which would have made the bearer look less like a mobile service engineer and more like some sort of crazed gynaecologist.

The only thing missing is a waxwork of an engineer in a blue suit, white shirt and tie diligently working through his fix list procedure, ideally with another waxwork of a sweaty and increasingly agitated client clutching the door frame. And of course the soundtrack of one of those mighty beasts and its whirring tapes and clunking buttons.

Through another room, and we hit the PC era, with racks of beige boxes along one side, from the first IBM PC through PS/2 and beyond. The range extends at least as far as 2005, when the x86 client business was offloaded to Lenovo. Facing off against them are the vendor's erstwhile notebook offering, ThinkPads, including keyboard-free touchscreen devices dating back as far as 1993. Like that was ever going to catch on.

The racks of now-obsolete personal computing kit in particular pose hosts of questions. These devices had a fraction of today's power, but this writer at least remembers how cutting edge and revolutionary they were when they were released – feel the might of the 486 – giving buyers that sliver of competitive edge that justified the thousands of pounds they cost back in the 1980s and 1990s. How quickly obsolescence comes around.

Still clocking on: Terry Muldoon
Photo: Joe Fay

Food for thought for the site's latest crop of cutting edge developers surely? Apparently not. Asked if Hursley's inmates like to take a trip downstairs to gaze at the racks of ATs or ThinkPads or green screen terminals for inspiration, McLean is blunt. "No, I wouldn't say they do."

"They're historical things, right?" he continues. "They're not going to shed new light on the world or anything else. You can reflect on things – that people made decisions at different points in time. It's more that you can see those opportunities at different times then."

It's a fine balance. Focus remorselessly on the future, and be in danger of forgetting the mistakes of the past? Or continually fight yesterday's war, even as others create a new future around you. It's a dilemma for any technology company. You might have your own view on Big Blue's history, but it will probably ask you to name any other IT companies that have been around for over 100 years.

As we emerge from the bowels of the oldest part of the house, glimpsing into rooms bursting with un-catalogued or unrestored IBM kit, Muldoon mentions the strong rooms maintained by the various families who owned Hursley. One remains unopened apparently.

From there, it's back into the 21st century, or as IBM calls it, the Emerging Technology Services Lab. This is where those people with titles like "senior inventor" live, or at least demonstrate their most interesting projects. The day we arrived, demos were heavily focused on the internet of things, including a walk-through on a system for integrating building plans, service requests, sensors, and manuals. This included augmented reality overlays of manuals and repair procedures. The kind of thing you see demonstrated for M in the latest Bond movies? Chances are the plumber at MI6 will be using it first.

Remote healthcare was another hot topic. When the City of Bolzano in Italy decided to pitch itself as a retirement destination, it called in IBMers from Hursley to examine ways of monitoring the oldies without having to provide each with a personal butler. The result is a huge degree of instrumentation, monitoring health as well as more tangible issues, such as utility use, carbon monoxide and the like. The aim is to both maintain a more holistic picture of the residents' health and ensure scarce human resources are targeted more accurately.

Node-RED, another Hursley-developed technology, is a visual development environment to connect devices such as sensors, and link them into other systems – a tool to help "wire" the internet of things. It is based on the

MQ technology which underpins more traditional machine-to-machine communications, and which was developed at Hursley.

If you want to get truly bleeding edge, consider the use of brainwaves as computer interface. It was in service of this concept that your reporter found himself with a headset strapped to his bonce and told to empty his mind and then control a remote control car. Years of covering technology meant your reporter emptied his mind so well he forgot to film his subsequent mental driving escapades – although he did manage to get a snap of the onscreen code that represented his virtual brain dump.

So, Hursley shows us the future of IBM, and technology, as well as the past but what about the present?

You'll be happy to know that there are real developers working on real present day technology. As we said, Hursley is home to CICS and MQ development as well as a chunky amount of IBM's Java development. But again, this is an R&D lab, where the real world does overlap with the future. Thus Gerry Reilly, development director and CTO, IBM Messaging, was happy to wax lyrical about the technology's leap from its roots buried in pipelines and other difficult-to-reach applications and into our cars and fridges.

MQ's domain has traditionally been SCADA-type systems, oil pipelines and the like - seriously important, but off the radar of technology's cool kids and gadget heads, except for the more extreme security nuts. Reilly chuckles as he contemplates how the last few years have seen the same sort of architectures supporting networks of sensors, often from "hobbyists".

Now, he says, IBM is currently working with serious players in the automotive and white goods sectors, while the principles are being applied in areas such as modelling weather. "A lot of it is being driven by business partners."

Sadly, he wasn't able to tell us from which fridge we should be buying if we want to ensure our eating habits are borged into big data analytics systems. IBM has poured cash into acquiring analytics firms over the last six years. It's almost as if it had taken a long-term view of where technology was going to be heading in the twentyteens and taken a big bet on it.

While Reilly acknowledges that the instrumentation of so much of our every-day life throws up myriad cultural, privacy and legal implications, this is for society and business partners to thrash out: "IBM is not going to take a position." But it will develop and sell you the technology to take your own.

If that gives us plenty to think about as we criss-cross the site, we can distract ourselves by ruminating on the development of business architecture over the last 40 years. One minute you feel like you're in a 1970s newly built poly, the next that you're on the set of The Office. The site really seems to straddle multiple eras – just as the original house does.

Our last stop of the day brought things right up to date, as we hit Client Centre, overseen by Mike Sexton. This is what you're most likely to see if you're part of the IBM ecosystem – ie, a reseller, developer or customer. Or at least a potential part.

Whereas the museum covers the IBM customer as it was, the partner centre shows today's customer what their technology could be. The focus isn't really on legacy, but rather on the sleekest top-end IBM kit, including its latest mainframes, as well as its POWER Systems.

It's like looking into Harvey Nics' window for techies: everything is sleek, black, well-lit and behind glass. It's how the data centre of your dreams looks - no boxes of tapes or bags of cables lying around on the floor, no jars of ear-plugs attached to the wall.

However, the aim is to allow customers, partners and developers to experiment and see how IBM software or kit might fit their requirements. If those requirements mean some legacy kit to slow things down - well someone could always haul out a token ring network from the museum if you really wanted.

If that's all a bit bare metal for your liking, the centre has a series of "industry labs" showing just how IBM technology can feed into real world apps.

So you can also fantasise about being a global baddie, or attempting to defeat the same, in the centre's own "situation room", complete with banks of consoles, big screens and conference table. IBM has built a much larger situation room for the municipal government of Rio de Janeiro, so the proof of the pudding will be in the eating during the World Cup and Olympics. Another room focuses on crime, highlighting the predictive technology IBM claims has helped actual cops catch actual bad guys in the act.

IBM's vision of the modern home includes an array of smart meters bursting out of a dresser beneath a flock of geese. Opening one of the cupboards below unleashes a flock of smart meters. It's somewhere between Coronation Street and Brookside, rather than Downton. There's no hint of a robot butler to tactfully suggest one might want to turn down the heating; rather IBM envisions smart meters combining with utility firm's analytics systems to keep you updated via the TV.

If you've shaved a few pennies off your fuel bill, you might want to go shopping. And there is of course a retail lab, showing how IBM tech can underpin the entire retail experience, from campaign management, promotions and e-commerce to point of sale. One of the technologies underpinning the demo is called Tealeaf. It analyses why transactions aren't completed - though of course to this London-based writer, it sounds like a security application at best.

It's slightly eerie, sitting there towards the end of a winter's day, looking at "the future", with shelves full of fake salad and cheese, and sealed but empty wine bottles and cereal packets. You feel that if you opened one of the cereal boxes you'd find blue goo.

But there's another eerie aspect to this ersatz retail experience. Time was when you walked into a shop, it was a fair bet the scanner had an IBM logo on it. Not now. IBM moved out of that business a long time ago, just as it has moved on from laptops, notebooks and printers, not to mention the display and disk-based storage technologies where Hursley in particular forged ahead.

So, as McLean says: "You have to be willing to change and accept that the market changes and the world changes. Against that backdrop you've got to innovate."

He continues with the happy brutalism of the engineer: "You... have to walk away from things that you potentially invented... When we stepped away from punch cards, we were making a huge amount of money from that business but you know when you look to the future, you have to accept that occasionally you have to walk away from businesses."

And perhaps that's one of the true wonders of Hursley: a place where the future is designed even as 20-year-old technology is prepared for display in the museum, while just a few feet away, 50-year-old technology is tweaked to ensure today's mobile and cloud-based tech keeps on ticking over.

It's arguably a much more realistic alternative to the all-or-nothing year zero approach of many tech startups. Though we still miss the butler.

GPS
51.0268375,-1.3986139

Postcode
SO21 2JN

Getting there
Car: A3090 from either Winchester or Romsey. From Winchester, look for the 'Hursley' village sign and immediately turn right into the IBM entrance. From Romsey, turn left at the Poles Land junction on to the unmarked entrance of Hursley Park and continue for one mile to Hursley House. Public transport: Train from Waterloo to Winchester then 66 bus via Hursley to Romsey, getting off at Hursley Village Post Office, cross road follow path behind church and follow signs. Hursley is 15 minutes by taxi from station.

Entry
The museum is not open to the general public, group visits can be arranged.

National Physical Laboratory
Middlesex

Gavin Clarke

GEEK'S
GUIDE
TO BRITAIN

Measure for measure: The most applied-physicist-rich building in the UK

Scientific Gods of (very) small Things

Shielded by lime trees in a quiet corner of south-west London, a low, modern building constructed of green glass sits on rolling lawns behind a high metal fence.

It's a discreet facility save for a huge white sign facing the road with a blue official crest and three large letters that spell out NPL – the National Physical Laboratory.

The sign, the crest and high fence all suggest some sort of secret government research facility, camouflaged by obscurity amidst the leaves of London – the stuff of John Wyndham or *Dr Who*'s Brigadier Alistair Gordon Lethbridge-Stewart.

This low-rise building comprises more than 380 laboratories and claims to be the UK's largest employer of applied physicists.

What this is, though, is one of the planet's centres of excellence on testing and measuring. Testing and measuring what? Everything.

NPL is so good at testing and measuring, it has become the place to which government, industry and even other scientists turn to get things right. The result is that NPL has become embedded in history.

It was NPL that determined a more precise value for g (acceleration due to its gravity) in 1960 – calculated at 9.8118177 metres per second squared.

It was the body the UK Air Ministry turned to for critical tests on the

Supermarine S.6 seaplane racer during the 1920s, helping it to win the coveted Schneider Trophy. Good thing, too: the design experience gained by Supermarine was later used in the manufacture of the famous Spitfire fighter, of which more than 20,000 were made. The Spitfire, along with the Hawker Hurricane, was crucial to Britain's ability to send Hitler's Luftwaffe into a tailspin during World War II.

It was the experts at NPL who weighing Concorde supersonic airliner in 1979, ensuring it conformed with the Civil Aviation Authority's rules. Scales calibrated by NPL were positioned beneath each of Concorde's wheels to gauge the weight to within +/-3kg. The final weigh-in: 78,700kg.

NPL invents, too. Among its claims to fame: the first functioning atomic clock in 1955 and packet-switching in 1966 - a building block of the internet.

If all NPL had done, and does today, is weigh, test and measure, this would be a short story. But NPL has been and remains deeply involved in the units of measurement themselves - in making them more precise.

A more accurate second? Check. A reliable kilogram standard? That, too.

Seconds? Kilograms? Aren't these supposed to be givens, writ in stone? We learned them in school and put them into practice every day without thinking.

Actually, they aren't written in stone and NPL's physicists have worked for decades towards ever more precise definitions. NPL gave us the atomic clock, but now it's going further: working with laser-based time keeping to put an extra decimal point on the current definition of the second – defined as the rate at which caesium atoms flip when agitated by microwaves at a set frequency.

This obsession with the meticulous means NPL has become one of the world's timekeepers. The mega-lab is jointly responsible for maintaining Universal Co-ordinated Time (UTC), the world's time standard since 1972 and the mechanism upon which all clocks and anything with a timepiece in it relies.

UTC is a weighted average of International Atomic Time (TAI), which is the product of more than 200 atomic clocks in 50 labs worldwide - among them, NPL. So precise is NPL's atomic clock, though, that it's one of just six labs relied upon to keep an eye on the accuracy of UTC.

If only there were some way to get a peek behind the scenes at this? There is - albeit rarely. NPL isn't top-secret and hush-hush and it does plenty of outreach to local schools, but for the general public you must wait for one of its rare open days, such as World Metrology Day on 20 May, when the masses get to wander the labs and probe NPL's boffinry.

World Metrology Day commemorates the 1875 Metre Convention that established the metre and the kilogram as international standards – two of the units by which NPL lives and dies - and that saw these two units cast as physical objects, a metal bar and a solid cylinder both of platinum iridium.

The platinum iridium kilogram is still with us today – protected beneath two glass bell jars at the International Bureau of Weights and Measures (BIPM) just outside Paris. NPL is home to one of the working copies of that original, Number 18. The metal metre bar was replaced in 1960 by an atomic calculation based wavelengths.

I got a peek behind the lab doors with the manager of NPL outreach - Andrew Hanson.

NPL's TARDIS-like new building, completed in 2003
Photo: Gavin Clarke

The buildings that housed most of that early work – such as the testing of the Spitfire – have gone as the work moved on to new fields. All that remains of that past is Bushy House, a country pile in Teddington, where NPL was first based in 1902, shortly after its creation in 1900 by the Royal Society.

What you tour today is the new building, completed in 2003. Inside it is like the TARDIS: corridor upon corridor, room upon room. Some offices look more corporate than science – glass walls and office furniture – while others are exactly what you imagine when you think "laboratory": reinforced doors and spotless white rooms. Some labs, though, are not at all what you'd imagine as places of science, as I'll get to in a second. The number of doors sporting signs warning of radiation and lasers whip past so fast on the tour they become a blur.

The first set of labs we come to belong to NPL's acoustics department. Here they test sound and noise and the equipment to capture and measure both - 6,000 tests a year. Tested systems are deployed in areas where there's a strong legal requirement to make sure readings are accurate. They work on everything from testing the sensitivity of microphones used in medicine to devices used to measure noise pollution. They've worked with at least one food manufacturer to test the loudness of the crunch of their biscuits.

Tests are so stringent, the calibration work by NPL provides a reference standard used to calibrate other people's microphones. NPL claims to achieve minimal inaccuracy on sounds quieter than the level of human hearing at 0.03 dB on mics in the range of 2Hz to 25kHz. Every test that goes out of the lab can be tracked back to ensure accountability, with data queried via spreadsheet or text file.

"We send mics around the world," acoustics group higher research scientist Janine Avison told us. "We are one of 12 labs that measure and we compare the results of our testing rigs."

The particular room we're in looks rather ordinary: white and spotless with work benches and sockets. In the corner sits a rig sprouting wires which relies on software built by NPL to perform pressure measurements on microphones. NPL differs from most other labs, which use an off-the-shelf reciprocity system from a Danish company called Bruel & Kjaer.

The setup measures air pressure, temperature and humidity; there's a signal generator and two lock-in amplifiers combined with the microphones, their pre-amplifiers and their power supplies. "Powerful" software tools are used to isolate and examine every part of the calibration in detail, Avison says.

Next, we visit NPL's Large Pressure Tank, which is used to calibrate hydrophones and sonar transducers - which turn electrical signals into sound. Such equipment is used in areas such as testing and measuring underwater noise pollution in the range of 1kHz and 1MHz.

NPL has two tanks but we view the larger – 5.5 metres in diameter and 5 metres deep.

This is one of those NPL laboratories I mentioned that doesn't look like a science lab. This one looks more like the inside of a nuclear reactor chamber: a large almost empty floor space save for portals that let you peek down into deep, green-blue coloured water beneath and with various pieces of equipment ready to glide about the top.

This is a split-level lab, though; go out of the door, down a flight of stairs, open a grey-white set of doors and you find yourself squeezing into a room full of a huge metal frame and massive wooden barrel. It contains the Large Pressure Tank's 80 tons of water that we were just gazing into.

The whole setup includes a submarine-line Acoustic Pressure Vessel used to simulate ocean conditions that can be pressurised to simulate depths of up to 700m and temperatures of between 2° to 35°C.

Finally, we peek into two rooms that couldn't be more different: the reverberation room and the hemi anechoic (echo-free) chamber.

The reverberation room has five sides and no parallel surfaces – the idea being to make sound waves travel further and last longer than normal. It's a large room, 330 cubic meters in size, and the wonky walls, complete with a single lightbulb hanging from the ceiling, make this feel rather like being on the set of a German Expressionist film from the 1920s.

The room's properties are enhanced by its construction – thick concrete coated with extra-hard plaster to help minimise sound absorption. The whole room rests on a series of thick, block-like shock absorbers and sits inside a larger room for total isolation from outside interference.

A single B2 musical note, which has a frequency of 125Hz, can last up to 29.9 seconds in here. A mumble travels a long way and you find yourself whispering in conversation just to avoid getting an ear bashing. Avison reveals a little secret about the reverberation chamber: she sometimes sings in here.

The reverberation room is used to measure the noise absorption properties of different materials in areas like soundproofing and to calibrate equipment like microphones.

The hemi anechoic chamber is the opposite of the reverberation room. It's an echo-free room and feels like talking while nestling beneath a duvet. The room has a clear floor space of six by six metres, with the walls and ceiling lined by sound-absorbing fibreglass wedges. Like the reverberation room, the hemi anechoic chamber floats within a large room on a series of springs and is accessed by a heavy door to isolate it further.

Tests here are conducted in the range of 125Hz to 20kHZ – from roughly the pitch of an average male voice to a range beyond the hearing of most adults. The room is used for sound power measurements, microphone testing and has been used by at least one food manufacturer to test the crunch of their biscuits for loudness.

Next is another one of those laboratories that's probably a departure from the mental picture you had of a "lab". This one is more metal or wood workshop, filled with benches, various construction apparatus, building materials and models of different sizes.

En route we stop at the office of the man in charge - Nick McCormick, principal research scientist in NPL's advanced engineering materials group.

McCormick pulls a cardboard box from under his desk and pops open the flaps to show us the contents: row upon row of hard disks, still in their shiny silver wrappers, packed in like virgin ammunition. It's 100TB of storage.

Seven atomic clocks and four hydrogen masers monitor NPL's time signal.
Photo: Gavin Clarke

Why so much? The answer lies in McCormick's workshop, home to a temporary mock-up of a brick underground tunnel, with rails and metal dolly sporting 12 digital single lens reflex (SLR) cameras armed with four flash guns.

This is not automated papping, but rather a project to test the wear-and-tear of buildings, specifically cracks and gaps in tunnels.

"We are trying to make tunnel inspection easier," McCormick said. "We want to be able to compare different images and identify areas of change."

Currently, it's standard procedure for engineers inspecting tunnels to wander along armed with a camera on their hard hats and a stick, tapping the walls playing a game of "spot the difference" and listening to the sound for signs of wear. NPL is working with Network Rail to adopt the system we're looking at. The train company has 300km of tunnels, meaning its engineers do a lot of walking and tapping and generally guessing.

McCormick's answer to this is a system based on digital image correlation. It involves taking lots of very large photos very quickly and using software he built to compare new and old images.

The cameras in NPL's tunnel trolley take 12 shots per metre at 10/1000s of a second, with 24 megapixels per shot to deliver an image where one pixel covers one millimetre of tunnel, letting experts drill down to between a 10th and a 20th of a millimetre. Each image is 125 Gigapixels in size. A laser scanner on the front of the aluminium trolley measures the tunnel's shape.

Images are aligned over the full field, with two images compared at the pixel and sub-pixel level using McCormick's software. About 15,000 calculations are made per pixel for comparison: for two scans of a 500-metre long tunnel that means about 10 trillion calculations.

McCormick's program is written in Java and runs on his Mac Pro, using 20 simultaneous computational threads on two six-core processors. NPL's man reckons the software uses some highly efficient algorithms to run quickly and consume just 24GB of RAM. But the boffin does have a second Mac Pro in his office, plus four Mac Minis at his disposal – meaning 38 cores are available for processing.

Testing the stress on structures is an idea the mega-lab has used before – on buildings, and even on food. NPL worked with one chocolate giant to test how far the brown stuff shrank in the moulds to ensure that it fell out properly during manufacture. This process involved sprinkling an aluminium powder on the surface of hot chocolate and recording the changes as the bars shrank.

We leave here and journey next to the centre of time - a room where NPL keeps the physical and digital worlds running on time: the timescales laboratory.

Controversial NPL physicist Louis Essen created the world's first functioning atomic clock in 1955 - the Caesium 1. Mk 1 and its successor, the CSF2, have helped create and maintain TAI (Temps Atomique International, or International Atomic Time), which is used to calculate UTC. CSF2 is an atomic fountain, a cascade of caesium atoms. The second is measured using a process that takes place when the caesium atoms are exposed to microwaves: spin flip. The caesium atoms are resonated using microwaves until they flip at a specific frequency – 9,192,631,770 Hz; a flip defines a second.

This process is a reliable constant, making TAI and UTC more accurate than solar time, which is based on the Earth's rotation. That rotation is slowing.

An atomic-based definition of the second is perfect for digital devices and computers that need constants to function reliably just to keep time or help work out their location. The CSF2 in NPL today is 300,000 times more precise than Mk1, which - translated - means it loses just one nanosecond every two months and it has been named the most accurate atomic timepiece on the planet. As such, CSF2 is one of just six atomic clocks considered reliable enough to ensure the accuracy of UTC.

As for CSF2, it looks like an aluminium alcohol still on stilts while the room it occupies feels like a broom cupboard - tiny and windowless and nearly silent except for the ticking of tiny mechanisms on a workbench which are constantly raising and lowering their little arms to control the flow of the lasers that are used by the clock.

Upstairs from CSF2 is ground zero for time-keeping: the timescales laboratory. This is where the signals are prepared, sent outside NPL and monitored. It is from this room that UTC (NPL) – accurate to within 100 nano seconds (100 billionths of a second) – and the MSF Radio Time Signal are generated. The latter is the basis of the UK's civil time and is used to manage all manner of electronic devices but is best recognised as the pips heard on BBC Radio. Rare outages, when they occur thanks to maintenance, are noteworthy.

The signal is sent to the Anthorn Radio Station in Cumbria from whence it is broadcast across the UK. A long-wave signal is also sent to a station in Droitwich and broadcast by a BBC Radio 4 long-wave transmitter that dates from before World War II.

For all this not inconsiderable importance, it's a tiny and rather unassuming room: white walls, gentle lighting and a server-rack-like metal frame in the middle of the floor.

In another world, it would hold server blades. But packed in this rack is the gear to monitor the MSF time signal, check the UTC signal generated by NPL and send it up to Cumbria. A recent addition is a dedicated fixed link to the City of London's financial traders so they can time-stamp trades.

Overall, there are seven atomic clocks and four hydrogen masers. In this room there is one maser, packed into a black unit that makes it look like a sound system. A further three reside in a temperature-controlled lab downstairs. The one maser is the master clock for UK time with the others on back-up duties. As one final precaution, the maser is checked against CSF2.

We leave the atomic-clock section and enter another of those non-lab-looking labs. This reminds me of a Wickes' warehouse: high ceiling, brick dust on the floor, brooms propped up in different corners.

Curiously, too, square panels of cemented brick walls have been bolted between blue metal frames and are lined up awaiting some experimentation.

Rising above this scene is a giant aluminium cube waiting to receive them – it's contained by a round blue metal rig and controlled from a simple yellow box.

This is NPL's Hot Box facility and the silver box dominating the room is one of NPL's two "Guarded Hot Boxes". Hot boxes are used to measure transfer of energy as heat through various materials. The mega-lab has designed and built its own - and this one is capable of rotating. With the addition of rotation, NPL can test this transfer, and thereby the energy efficiency of materials, in any orientation: inserted materials can be warm on top and cold underneath, vice versa, or with a plain old left-to-right shift.

NPL has been testing heat transfer through materials since the 1970s and structures since the 1980s, but this rotating box was finished in 2002.

Ray Williams, principal research scientist in the materials processing and performance group, tells us the purpose of this rig is to get a grip on the energy efficiencies of different building materials - hence all those bricks lined up waiting for testing. It's designed to put some solid numbers behind claims by the construction sector on the energy efficiency of buildings and support the Government's Green Deal.

"Every wall, roof and floor in the country has been calculated," Williams tells us, meaning the heat-leaking properties of walls and roofs in the UK have been arrived at using the different mathematical formulas. Not in the hot box. "We measure the difference... we want to get the actual value of a brick wall."

How does this hot box work? It contains two chambers, whose temperatures can range from 22°C to a nippy −10°C. Materials are placed in the centre and measurements taken of the direction and rate of energy flow.

The hot box contains more than 140 sensors to log 250 channels of data every two hours on air temperature, airflow rates, fan power, transfer coefficient and thermal transmittance, as well as conductance and resistance. Data is logged using a program written by NPL that calculates all the parameters and measures thermal equilibrium. Data is stored in a text file and recalculated using an Excel spreadsheet.

It can take up to three days just for the materials to reach a state of equilibrium – where they stop absorbing energy as heat - and testing can begin. Some tests have taken up to three weeks to conduct – as in the case of insulated concrete.

Our tour finishes where so much of this began, in 1875 – with the kilogram. We're standing in a lab full of waist-high work benches that is spotlessly clean and seems impossibly bright. I find myself blinking. There are weights and measures everywhere, lined up in neat rows in wooden trays and under the cover of glass or perspex. We are here to see kilogram mass No 18 and its possible replacement, a silicon sphere.

Scientific researcher Stuart Davidson holds them in purple-gloved hands in this exceptionally clean environment. The gloves are designed to keep the weights free of contaminating fingerprints that might inadvertently alter the official mass as we know and use it.

The kilogram was one of the two first base units to be defined along with the metre - created following the signing of the Convention du Mètre (Treaty of the Metre) and formation of the Bureau of Weights and Measures (BIPM) in 1875.

The treaty was the result of years of pushing by France for an internationally recognised system of weights and measures - it had advocated this since the 1789 revolution. Pre-revolutionary France had had a system of 250,000 weights and measures that varied between villages, towns, cities and regions. It was chaotic and crippling for the economy. Britain had an archaic system, too, dating back to Roman times. Britain eventually signed up to the Convention in 1884 with the help of the Royal Society.

The second, kelvin, ampere, candela and mole were all ratified as standards in 1889. Over the years they've become atomic standards similar to the metre (wavelength) and have been rebranded as SI standards. Only the kilogram is holding out – the last to still be officially measured using a physical object. It's that mass that squats under glass at the BIPM outside Paris, France. It has held out despite decades of work to convert it into an atomic equation.

NPL worked on a Watt Balance to express the kilogram as an electrical current that plays on mass, voltage and movement. This work has moved to Canada and continues, with the US National Institute of Standards and Technology (NIST) also working on its own, separate Watt Balance.

So far, the difference in results between the two has been too great for an official standard - 250 parts per billion. The General Conference on Weights and Measures in Paris is overseeing the process and waiting to adjudicate: it wants accuracy of 20 parts per billion. To give you an idea of what's at stake, the mass in Paris is believed to have altered by just 50 parts per billion during its lifetime.

Look out for the next open day. This being a working facility and not generally open to the public, there's no café you can pop into for refreshments. No shop either. You can, though, walk into Teddington, which has plenty of restaurants and cafes – and shopping. A little further afield, but still close, is Kingston upon Thames. Should you choose to linger longer, there is a Travelodge next to the station, and you could pack NPL in with a family trip to Bushy Park or Hampton Court, too.

Whether you're chewing on your lunch or riding the train out after, marvel and be thankful for NPL. Its men and women are sweating the small stuff so you don't have to.

GPS
51.427120, -0.344186

Postcode
TW11 0LW

Getting there
By train:30-40 minutes from London Waterloo to Teddington, then a short walk or even shorter bus ride - 285 or R68 to Hampton Hill. By car: the A313 north of Kingston-upon-Thames

Entry
Check website for open-day events

Online resources
http://www.npl.co.uk/

The Great Aircraft Factory, Richmond Road, Kingston upon Thames

From 1918 to 1992 many thousands of aircraft and other vehicles were built here by Sopwith Aviation, Leyland Motors, Hawker Aircraft, Hawker Siddeley Aviation and BAe

1918 and 1919 - Sopwith Dolphin, Snipe and Salamander fighter aircraft
1920s and 30s - Trojan light cars and vans, Leyland Cub and Lynx lorries
1940s - Military equipment including Leyland Comet battle tanks
1950s - Hawker Sea Hawk and Hunter jet fighter aircraft

1960s, 70s and 80s - Hawker Siddeley/BAe Harrier vertical take-off and landing fighter aircraft
1970s and 80s.- Hawker Siddeley/BAe Hawk advanced jet training aircraft

Kingston Aviation Heritage Trust

Royal Kingston

www.kingstonaviation.org

Tommy Sopwith's Aviation Empire
Kingston upon Thames

Gavin Clarke

Kingston's aviation empire: from industry firsts to Airfix heroes

Sir Thomas Sopwith's suburban Surrey hub

He learned to fly aged 22, set up his first aircraft factory aged 24 and by 30 his fighters dominated the skies over the Western Front.

Thomas Octave Murdoch Sopwith - later, Sir – founded the Sopwith Aircraft Company in 1912, turning out aeroplanes from an Edwardian roller-skating rink in Kingston upon Thames. (Yes, the Edwardians had a love affair with roller skating.)

His firm and its successors notched up the firsts – float plane, tri-plane, British mono-wing fighter to exceed 300mph (482.8kph) , aircraft capable of taking off and landing vertically.

Some of these planes became legends: the Camel, best all-round fighter of World War I, the Hawker Hurricane, mainstay of the RAF during the Battle of Britain, the Hawker Tempest that duelled with Hitler's first jet fighters, and the Harrier jump jet – taking off and landing on the spot.

But while these aircraft were revolutionary, they were also practical. Thanks to their cunning designs and an efficient manufacturing operation, Sopwith achieved market saturation in World War I and, later, of the RAF and of British aviation.

The story of Sopwith isn't just the aircraft - it's also a tale of business risk. Sopwith liquidated Sopwith Aviation to rise again and buy rivals, first as HG Hawker Engineering and then Hawker Aircraft. He also pressed on with the Hurricane without getting any actual government orders.

His legacy? BAe Systems, the successor to those early firms: an £18bn global colossus employing 88,000 people, spanning diverse activities and today making the Hawk – flying the flag with the RAF aerobatic team, the Red Arrows.

The backdrop for this manufacturing success wasn't the industrial heartland of the Midlands but rather the market town of Kingston upon Thames, in leafy North Surrey.

Sopwith established not one but three factories in Kingston, meaning a small town in the commuter belt was responsible for the majority of fighter designs in World War I and, the heart of Britain's military aviation industry for years afterwards. He became one of Kingston's largest employers with a trio of factories plus research shop. Entire households became dependent on Sopwith's pay packets; over nine decades Sopwith and its successor firms is thought to have employed 40,000 in Kingston. A network of suppliers grew up, too, feeding parts, materials and services into those Kingston factories.

BAe closed the last site in the 1990s. All that's left today in the town are some random civic sculptures and streets bearing relevant names. Kingston University also runs undergraduate courses in aviation and has both a building and a scholarship named after Sopwith's top designer, Sir Sydney Camm.

The Register decided to tour Sopwith's former industrial town. We navigated the backroads searching for the lost buildings and former factory sites. Along the way we saw plenty of plaques on walls. These are the work of Kingston Aviation, which has been running events with Lottery Funding to raise awareness of Kingston's aviation past. Kingston Aviation is the work of ex-aircraft manufacturing engineer David Hassard, who we spoke to for this piece.

We started at the site of the Edwardians' roller skating rink on Canbury Park Road: the first of Sopwith's three Kingston plants.

Back then, Canbury Park Road had Victorian terraces down one side facing mansions on the other and at the top a 1900s single-storey cinema called the Cinema Palace which was replaced with a modernist bunker, the Regal Cinema, by the 1930s. The rink pressed its cheek up to the wall of both cinemas.

Today, the cinema is closed and the building houses a dance studio and TV shop around the side, with sprigs of Buddleia shooting from the brickwork. The rink and mansions are gone, knocked down for red-brick and green-glass offices.

It all feels post-industrial and sort of run down. A narrow alley runs between the cinema and the offices on what would have been the rink's entrance.

Back in 1912 the rink glowed with modern civic pride; arched windows and Art Nouveau signage on the front, looking like a conservatory. What lay behind was a space of 13,000ft^2 (1,207m^2) with a high roof and no internal columns: ideal for skating. Or for building aeroplanes.

What brought Sopwith here?

Educated in engineering, Sopwith was fascinated by almost anything with a motor and was taken with newfangled aeroplanes. Having learned to fly, he formed an aviation school in 1910 at Brooklands Airfield in Weybridge, 15 miles away. He was joined by two of the three brains that would help him design and deliver those first planes: Fred Sigrist, an engineer on Sopwith's yacht who became engineer and designer, and an Australian named Harry Hawker who'd worked at Daimler and became Sopwith's test pilot and co-designer.

Their first order - for the Sopwith Hybrid - came in 1912 from the Royal Navy. Having talked the talk, Sopwith and Co. had to deliver the goods. He needed a factory and so came to riverside Kingston. The Bat Boat that was also ordered by the Navy in 1913 was the first aircraft built in Kingston. It was also the first successful British flying boat.

Why pick a rural market town where retail (department store Bentalls opened its doors there in 1867) was the big thing?

Kingston had developed as an important post for trade and transport thanks to its history as a major Thames crossing point. This meant a workforce on tap skilled in building with wood – skills not dissimilar to those used in building the first aircraft.

Initially with just six workers, by the outbreak of World War I there were 150 staff squeezed into the rink - woodworkers, panel beaters and polishers, wirers, fitters and welders. Machinists hollowed out wood to make their aircraft's spars lighter, while others beat and fashioned metal brackets, bearings, flanges, plates and made fuel tanks.

Women sewed the linen fabric for the wings and bodies, painted dope on the fabric and varnished the wood and fuselage.

It was dangerous work and in those pre-health-and-safety days the women donned gloves to protect against blisters caused by the caustic dope and drank milk every day in the belief it would stop the powerful fumes damaging their lungs, according to Kingston Museum and Heritage Services.

As World War I developed and more men went to the front, women moved out of simply doping wing fabric and onto the shop floor, soldering, running presses and carrying out inspections so that by the final year of the war nearly a third of Sopwith's workforce of 3,500 were women.

Such was the pace of orders that Sopwith soon needed a bigger factory: he picked a site just 109 yards (99.6m) up the road, a facility that became the heart of his empire - at the corner of Canbury Park Road and Elm Crescent.

Surrounded by roads, this site became known as The Island. It began as a 14,000ft^2 (1,300.6m^2) shed in 1913 but by 1917 stretched to 40,000ft^2 (3,716m^2), was built from brick and reached up three storeys.

The Island was self-contained: it featured a sawmill, machine and sheet metal shops, tool stores, aircraft assembly floors and separate dope and paint shops. One whole wing – along the Canbury Park Road side – was dedicated to design while there were separate departments for sales, ordering and accounts. It was through these that orders for essentials such as engines and machine guns flowed.

From Canbury Park came the design of every one of Sopwith's aircraft between 1916 and 1958 – from biplane, to monoplane to jet aircraft.

This was the Henry Ford approach to aircraft production, coming at a time when most aircraft firms had one or two models that were delivered in small runs. And the results showed: 25 per cent of British fighter aircraft designs in World War I came from Sopwith and 60 per cent of all single-seater aeroplanes in the British and allied air forces were Sopwith. This includes models designed and built in Kingston or just designed in Kingston and built under licence elsewhere.

Kingston produced 16,237 aircraft of 32 designs for World War I. The best known of these is arguably the Camel, which made its maiden flight in December 1916 and during its relatively short time claimed more enemy aeroplanes than any other aircraft: 1,294. Just over 5,000 Camels were built – 550 in Kingston alone.

The Camel became a hit because it was a revolutionary aircraft, with a winning combination of firepower, speed and manoeuvrability.

In a design first, the Camel featured twin, forward-facing guns - a pair of .303" Vickers machine guns. It was a mounting that became an RAF standard. The guns used the fledgling synchronization gear technology, developed to allow fixed forward-firing guns to fire through the aircraft's propeller blades without shooting them off. Anything caught head-on by a Camel got a hot-lead shower.

The most common model of the Camel featured a nine-cylinder, 130 horse power Clerget air-cooled engine giving it a climb of 1,085 feet per minute (330.7m per minute)– double that of the German's Fokker D.II and nearly twice as fast as the D.III. It was faster, too, with a top speed of 118mph (189.9kph) and it could fly higher – touching 19,000 feet (5,791m).

What made the Camel so lethal was its manoeuvrability. Ninety per cent of the plane's weight - engine, fuel, guns, ammunition and pilot - were packed into the first seven feet of the fuselage, making it compact and finely balanced.

It wasn't perfect: front loading made the Camel fast on the turn but too fast for the inexperienced pilot. Pilots also had to combat a powerful clockwise rotary effect in the engine that made left turns nearly impossible and saw pilots forced to sweep right.

Kingston Aviation's Hassard credits the Camel's design and performance to the driving desire of Sopwith's chief test pilot, Hawker, who was a motorbike fanatic. "He wanted something so compact you could throw it around," Hassard told us.

It was a Camel pilot who was closely involved in the shooting down of Manfred von Richthofen, the infamous Red Baron with 81 allied kills and who flew a Fokker Dr.I triplane painted a brilliant red at the head of Germany's pre-eminent Flying Circus. Richthofen's Fokker was a copy of Sopwith's own triplane model; the Germans had studied one that crashed behind their lines. But, while the German three-winger was highly manoeuvrable it was slower than Sopwith's and it was dogged by structural failures, with the top wing prone to breaking.

The Camel features in a First World War Air Exhibition at the RAF Museum, Hendon, that opened in December 2014 to mark the war's 100th anniversary.

By 1917 Sopwith's factories couldn't keep up with demand. In April 1918, Sopwith opened his third Kingston plant - the then new National Aircraft Factory No. 2. The factory, which stood on a field near the Thames just outside Kingston and off Richmond Road, had been built by the Ministry of Munitions in just 26 weeks during the winter of 1917. Less than a mile away from Canbury Park Road, it was leased to Sopwith and became known as the Ham Factory.

The Island factory now Sopwith House with Sigrist Square behind
Photo: Gavin Clarke

The Ham Factory looked like a series of hangars squatting next to each other, and behind their huge front doors lay a cavernous belly. In here hundreds of Sopwith Snipes, Dolphins and Salamanders were lined up and churned out.

But Ham, or possibly peace, killed Sopwith's company. War finished seven months later, leaving Sopwith with piles of parts and unwanted orders.

Sopwith limped on, trying to retain his remaining 1,400 staff by switching them to produce civil aircraft and ABC motorcycles. Yet, faced by immediate repayment of wartime profits, Sopwith was liquidated in 1920 and Ham was sold to British lorry maker Leyland Motors for £227,000.

But this wasn't the end of Tom Sopwith, or his presence on Richmond Road: Sopwith was rebooted as H.G. Hawker Engineering in 1920 and he bought back the Ham Factory in 1948 for £585,000. I'll come back to that.

Back on our tour, I'm at the junction of Canbury Park Road and Elm Crescent looking at what's left of The Island. Now called Sopwith House and strictly residential, it's a Grade-II listed building.

You can walk a loop of the old Island. Sopwith House fronts a small, Brookside-like housing development called Sigrist Square. Sopwith House is part of Sigrist Square, behind a brick and iron fence featuring a motif of propeller blades. Look at the ends of Sopwith House and you can see where the new bricks join the old, where the building was cauterized after its other parts were cut off. Walk a few yards from the corner, down Canbury Park Road, and you find a pair of brick gateposts bearing two plaques from Kingston Aviation.

Come back to the corner of Canbury Park Road and Elm Crescent and you'll see a first-floor bay window – that was Sopwith's office. From the early 1920s to the 1930s the offices of Sopwith's chief designer, Sydney Camm, were behind the upstairs windows along Canbury Park Road.

Turn 180 degrees: breathing down your neck in this narrow road is a red brick, fort-like building fronted by high windows. This is Siddeley House, also listed.

Now leased offices owned by Search Office Space, in the 1930s this was Sopwith's Experimental Shop – used to develop top-secret projects. The first aircraft built here was the prototype Hawker Hurricane in 1935. Peek inside and you'll see the original block and tackle with runner in the ceiling and the dangling hook used to load lorries that pulled up to the spot where you're standing.

The Experimental Shop was self-contained: on different floors were canteen, fitters and assembly facilities. Space was tight, with large, semi-assembled parts passed between floors down the outside fire escapes.

Also developed in this building were the Hawker Henley, Hotspur, Tornado and Typhoon but it was the Hurricane that made the biggest hit.

Camm joined Sopwith's firm in 1923 becoming chief designer in 1925 and, in addition to working on more than 3,000 biplanes, started on an Air Ministry tender for a monoplane fighter.

Rivals at Supermarine – later Vickers-Armstrong – in Southampton were working on the Spitfire, too, but the Hurricane flew first, in November 1935, and entered mass production ahead of the Spitfire. The Hurricane also dominated the RAF's count of mono-wing fighters – outnumbering Spitfires at the pivotal Battle of Britain. Hurricanes scored more aerial victories, too, during that conflict: 1,593 of a total 2,739.

All this while Germany's Willy Messerschmitt had prototyped his Bf 109 in

1935. This became the Luftwaffe's lead fighter in the Battle of Britain but got its first combat experience in the Spanish Civil War, between 1936 and 1937.

The Hurricane was the epitome of Sopwith's design ethos: practical while scoring a number of firsts.

The Hurricane was the RAF's first fighter capable of exceeding 300mph. It featured a retractable undercarriage and had space for eight wing-mounted machine guns capable of firing without striking the propeller blades, doing away with synchronization mechanisms in the engine.

The aeroplane was tough with an engine capable of operating in all theatres of war – European, desert and tropical - while the Spitfire suffered engine problems outside Europe. It was light, too, being constructed in part using lighter-than-wood aluminium.

Camm, with Sopwith's managing director Sigrist in the 1920s, had developed and patented a technique using steel tube frames that helped ensure the overall airframe was light yet tough. They squared off tubes that were replacing wood as the structure of modern airframes so that they could be bolted together instead of welded. Bolting was critical: the quality of welding could vary, making it a potential weak spot.

Camm also took two important steps to ensure his Hurricane beat the Spitfire. One was to adapt the design of his existing Hawker Fury biplane. Another was employing a combination of wood and canvas with aluminium not just in the frame but also in the skin - a technique that helped spread weight and stress and, again, meant a lighter and less bulky airframe.

Camm's approach meant the Kingston production lines could accommodate the new model with relatively little disruption. Supermarine, working on the Spitfire, didn't have it so easy: it was building a new type of aeroplane with a completely aluminium frame, skin and wing design that used flush rivets for greater speed. It wasn't just a brand new aircraft – it was a brand-new manufacturing process, too, which caused problems in construction and helped ensure delays and missed deadlines.

"What he did was design for manufacturing; he made sure even though they were building the best aircraft, they could be built effectively and efficiently. He was keeping an eye from on top saying things like: 'Don't do that, we can't build that that quickly,' or: 'We can't build that time and time again,'" Hassard told *The Reg*.

For all that, the Hurricane was a gamble. Sopwith pressed into production on the first 600 fighters without actually ever receiving an order from the all-powerful Air Ministry – the customer. That meant investing in the people and the plant to produce a new aircraft with no guarantee of an actual buyer.

"They took a big risk," Hassard said. "That was Tommy Sopwith all over – he was a man who was very quick at taking decisions. A brilliant businessman for those reasons."

After the Hurricane, Camm went on to design the all-aluminium Tempest, the RAF's fastest fighter of World War II with a top speed of over 450mph (724kph), that played a major part in downing Germany's V1 flying bombs and Messerschmitt's jet-powered Me 262 – the world's first operational jet fighter, flying at 540mph (869kph).

It was during this period that the character of the Kingston plants changed, as aeroplanes went metal.

Kingston's woodworkers were slowly outnumbered by machinists shaping and making aluminium alloys and titanium; people treating metals to prevent corrosion; copper and pipe smiths; and tool makers who ensured the factories' machines made identical parts. Engineers worked on pneumatics and hydraulics in retractable landing gear on the emerging mono-wing fighters.

Hundreds of technicians were deployed on experimental work with test rigs to stress-test airframes through endless cycles of take offs and landings, checking for fatigue or engine failure. Boffins from the National Physical Laboratory (NPL), in Teddington, ran their slide rules over the planes, testing and recording performance in the facility's wind tunnels.

It sounded busy, but everything is relative: Hassard reckons this wasn't mass production as we'd know it today – the factories in Kingston turned out just a few dozen planes a month in the 1930s and one hundred Hurricanes a month during World War II.

But it was enough: at some points during the 1930s up to 80 per cent of the aircraft serving in the RAF were Sopwith-designed. Sopwith's company was a cash-flow positive as a result of the business, and he bought up rivals including Gloster Aircraft, maker of the nippy little Gladiator biplane fighter, and later a manufacturing plant for Hurricanes and Typhoons. He also bought Lancaster-Bomber maker Avro. During this period, through a spate of acquisitions, H G Hawker Engineering became Hawker Aircraft.

At the end of World War II, as Sopwith's factories turned to jets, it was clear Canbury Park was too small. Following a brief search, in 1948 Sopwith bought the Ham Factory he'd had to surrender 28 years earlier.

It's here that our tour goes back up Canbury Park Road, past the rink, and heads north up the Richmond Road/A307 to the site of that factory. In the car, you'll need to navigate Kingston's one-way maze to get back onto the A307. Or you can take the No 65 bus from Kingston station and get off at Tudor Drive.

Ham spanned 47 acres so you need to make two stops. First, up to the junction of the A307 and Dukes Avenue. If in the car, turn left and pull into Northweald Lane; if bus, get off at Tudor Drive and walk a short distance. This is the start of a village in all but name; an estate of neat homes and eddying lanes with names like Camel Grove built on half of the old factory site. Head back to the corner and at the junction you'll find a brick pillar bearing two stainless steel plaques from Kingston Aviation marking the location's significance and featuring a Harrier – one of the main aircraft built there.

Get back in the car, or walk past the Tudor Drive stop, and travel a few hundred yards back down the A307, turn right onto Lower Ham Road and you end up at a sports field and the YMCA Hawker Centre. This is the other half of the Ham Factory – the half that didn't fall to developers.

To the right, the field runs up against the wall marking the housing estate we just left. Ahead and to the left, the YMCA Hawker Centre. On the right-hand wall of the centre inside the reception is a bronze commemorative plaque. Go in and turn right, past the reception and you'll find a glass wall bullet-pointing the history.

Back outside and standing on the sports field, you'll have to imagine Sopwith's factory surrounded by a cluster of busy offices and facilities.

It was 1958 when the focus shifted from Canbury Park to here as the design office moved into Ham. It was also the year when Richmond Road received a massive facelift, acquiring a brand-new façade that was reputedly the work of the architect who'd designed the Milk Marketing Board's offices in nearby Thames Ditton. It was a grand exterior of tall windows and towering columns looking more like some suburban municipal offices rather than an HQ of national defence.

The only thing that gave anything away was a humble wooden sign reading

Hawker Siddeley Aviation Limited, then British Aerospace Company, and then just British Aerospace when the company's name changed again in 1977 following mergers with other British aircraft makers and nationalisation by the then Labour government.

In addition to design and build were test facilities, including the "Mithraeum" structural test frame to strength- and fatigue-test large parts such as entire airframes. Additional testing equipment put fuel, hydraulic, flying and electrical systems through their paces.

It was Ham that became the manufacturing centre for another first in aviation: the world's first viable vertical takeoff and landing (VTOL) aircraft.

That VTOL aircraft was the Hawker P.1127, which evolved into the Harrier. Nearly 1,000 Harriers were built - a seemingly small number, but they made an impact. Harriers were ordered and adapted by the Royal Navy and the RAF. Harriers were also ordered by US forces, normally served by their own defence contractors. Harriers flew with the US Marine Corps under a design produced by US giant McDonnell Douglas and BAe. The last 74 Harriers were only retired by the Brits in 2011 – and they were bought at fire-sale prices by the USMC for parts to keep their Harrier II fleet airworthy.

The Harrier saw combat two decades after entering service in 1969, during the Falklands War against Argentina in 1982. A total of 26 Harriers and Sea Harriers were embarked on the Royal Navy aircraft carriers HMS Invincibleand HMS Hermeson the mission to recapture the Falklands. Their presence helped stop the Argentinians inflicting heavy losses on the British task force so close to the Argentinian mainland and military machine.

As it was, Argentinian aircraft struck 17 ships, sinking five warships and one civilian vessel, the Atlantic Conveyor. Of the Harriers, five were lost – two to bad weather – in return for 20 Argentinian aircraft downed.

The Harrier found a niche in military planning – short take-off and landing, suited to the role in the Falklands; conceived to serve against the Soviets launching without airstrips from the forests of Europe. Some 14 Harriers had arrived in the Falklands packed on the decks of the Atlantic Conveyor- fortunately they had been flown off before she was sunk.

Work on the P.1127 started in 1957, in a Bristol outpost of what had become Sopwith's aviation empire. Michel Henry Marie Joseph Wibault developed the concept for a vertical and short take-off and landing (V/STOL) engine using a Bristol BE.25 Orion turboprop engine. Wibault's engine directed thrust down via two nozzles on the outside of the aircraft. The Orion power plant hailed from Sopwith's Bristol Siddeley firm.

The engine evolved to a more powerful BE.53 but Bristol needed help ironing out lingering technical problems – it also needed an airframe in which to mount the new engine. The firm approached Hawker and Camm, who suggested the addition of two extra external nozzles to direct the airflow, solving the problem of balance. The Hawker and Bristol teams began work on the P.1127 as a "high-speed helicopter".

NATO funded 75 per cent of the cost of developing the engine and the teams meshed. The British Ministry of Aviation ordered two prototypes and four developmental aircraft in 1960.

The P.1127 was actually designed at Canbury Park Road but built by hand at Richmond Road. The Harrier was a long way from the early biplanes: 200,000 components with a quality-control process that inspected things such as welding joints using X-ray systems. The work had become more specialized, too, giving rise to apprentices. Over time, aircraft bodies shifted from aluminium to carbon fibre.

"In this area of North Kingston there was hardly a family who didn't have somebody who worked there," Hassard says. "You couldn't get a more complete industry or broader range of skills."

The Ham Factory closed in 1992 and was knocked down after BAe pulled out of London and as the local authority succumbed to housing developers. The land was carved up between these developers building more than 300 homes, the council that owns the large field, and the Hawker Athletic Social Club.

According to Hassard grown men cried as the wrecking balls tore into the Ham Factory. It's not hard to see why, as you stand on the football pitch outside the Hawker Athletic Social Club and superimpose the image in your head of what was once on this now mostly wide-open vista.

Today, Richmond Road would have been turned into urban dwellings. At least the façade might have been retained, like at Canbury Park Road.

Like the factories, Sopwith and his team are gone, too. Harry Hawker died in a plane crash in 1921, Sigrist passed away in 1956 and Sydney Camm – knighted for his services to the nation's defence, like Sopwith - passed away in 1966.

Sopwith outlasted them all, dying in 1989. He retired from day-to-day business in 1963 and became board chairman. He was still there aged 90 and then made president for life of British Aerospace. BAe pulled out of the town where he'd started a few years after he passed and the wrecking balls flew.

We're at the end of our solo flight. Your best bet is to loop back to Kingston for refreshments and – if you want – shopping. There's a cinema and theatre, too, and lots of water-side bars and cafes.

My advice? Go riverside, near the theatre and where cheeky swans bob about waiting for passers-by to throw them pieces of bread, and reflect: reflect on the boat building business that helped lure Sopwith to Kingston, turning this rural market town into an industrial powerhouse.

GPS
Skating rink
51.413165, -0.299371

The Island and Siddeley House
51.413001, -0.298608

Post code
KT2 6LX

Richmond Road (YMCA Hawker Center)
51.427225, -0.308873

Post code
KT2 5BH

Getting there
By train: 30-40 minutes from London Waterloo to Kingston upon Thames, then a short walk from station. For the former Ham factory: Bus No. 65 bus from Kingston station, stop T towards Ealing Broadway and get off at Tudor Drive.

Entry
N/A

Online resources
www.kingstonaviation.org/
www.brooklandsmuseum.com
www.rafmuseum.org.uk/london/
www.rafmuseumstoryvault.org.uk
www.kingston.gov.uk/museum/

Goonhilly Satellite Earth Station
Cornwall

SA Mathieson

Suffering satellites! Goonhilly's ARTHUR REBORN for SPAAAACE

BT's sat comms site repurposed

Big data? Pah. Arthur is big hardware. He weighs in at 1,118 tons (1,135,940kg), has a diameter of 84.9ft (25.9m) and is 52 years old. From his home, a high plateau on Cornwall's remote Lizard peninsula – as far south as you can go on the island of Great Britain without falling off – he has played his part in Space Age history, appropriate given he resembles one of its rockets in scale and riveting style.

Officially known as Goonhilly 1, Arthur is one of the world's first satellite communication dishes. This is the dish that received the first transatlantic television pictures from the Telstar satellite on 11 July 1962, tracking it as it crossed the sky in just 22 minutes. And, in a very British touch, it is a Grade II-listed building.

Goonhilly was one of the world's first three satellite earth stations. Until a few years ago, it was also a tourist attraction run by BT, where visitors could see Arthur and friends and learn about the wonder of telecommunications, particularly those run by BT.

On a rainy summer day in West Cornwall, the Goonhilly Satellite Earth Station Experience with visitor centre was the harassed parent's last best hope.

Improvements in satellite technology and the renaissance of submarine cables meant Arthur was seen as a high-maintenance dinosaur and in 2006, BT decided to switch its international communications to submarine cables and two smaller dish farms in Herefordshire and London.

BT closed the visitor centre and planned to convert much of the site into a windfarm. Only Arthur's listed building status got in the way of its demolition.

Arthur now has a new owner – Goonhilly Earth Station Ltd (GES) – and Goonhilly is being repurposed for space exploration and other specialist applications. Arthur is about to start a new career in space science, as part of a project run by Britain's universities, 50 years after Telstar.

There are even plans for a new visitor centre. This is not open yet and – with the exception of a Segway course next to Arthur, £32.50 per person for 90 minutes – Goonhilly is currently closed to the public. But GES agreed to give *The Register* an early look at what it is doing in this remote corner of Britain.

Driving the ruler-straight eastern perimeter road past the offices of the rather "high-concept for a taxi-firm" Telstar Taxis, Goonhilly feels forbidding and deserted. The entrance barriers look like they guard a secret site, and a car looks small in a holding space designed for lorries. So far, this feels like a scene from a 1980s government conspiracy drama.

The General Post Office, forerunner of BT, chose this site for its position on the highest ground on the Lizard peninsula, with clear views west across the Atlantic, as well as to the south and east.

There are very few buildings nearby, the air is unpolluted, the weather generally good and there is little electrical interference. Geologically, the site's hard bedrock made it suitable for heavyweights like Arthur. The air feels strangely foreign, thanks to the Gulf Stream bringing moist warm currents up from the tropics.

BT continues to use the site for submarine cables – one of the most important, SeaWeMe3 which forwards traffic to Europe, the Middle East and Asia, calls in at Goonhilly. BT also continues to run the site's security, meaning I have to check in with a BT guard behind a glass screen to make progress. My name is on the list, so equipped with a plastic badge I drive along more deserted road, with signs in the swirly font that BT discarded several years ago.

The *Edge of Darkness* vibe lifts on reaching Goonhilly's control centre – which on my visit, in blazing autumnal sunshine, featured glaziers fitting new windows while listening to Steve Wright on Radio 2.

When re-opened, visitors will be able to watch the work inside the control centre, hence the new windows. Inside, a team of students from nearby

Falmouth University's Alacrity graduate programme are working on developing and building a multiplayer game that will allow teams of four people to control a virtual space mission from Nvidia Shield gaming tablets.

When the centre reopens, families and suits in corporate groups will be able to escape bad weather by saving the International Space Station – or creating *Gravity*-style orbital havoc.

Ian Jones is chief executive of GES and he designed and built some of Goonhilly's equipment when he worked for British computer pioneer Ferranti. For my trip, I spoke to Jones; he tells me that when BT announced the site's closure, he and former colleagues saw "an amazing potential" to turn it into a mixed-use site, taking advantage of the equipment and infrastructure already in place. The dish's monstrous size makes it ideal for capturing and helping track signals from deep space – both natural and artificial, Jones says.

In January 2011, GES agreed with BT to lease the antennas with an option to buy the whole site. Three years later, having increased business and raised private equity funding, it exercised that option. The deal includes BT leasing back a few areas of Goonhilly, including the part that houses its sub-sea cable station.

Arthur and Guinevere (aka Goonhilly 3) are joining a dispersed group of dishes known as an interferometer network – appropriately called e-Merlin – run by a consortium of British universities, with antennas at Jodrell Bank in Cheshire - also a stop on the Geek's Guide tour and in Cambridge.

Goonhilly has agreed with the UK's Joint Academic Network (JANET) to install a dedicated 10Gb/s fibre link to Jodrell Bank, and Manchester University will fit a new receiver to Arthur in 2015. GES is sponsoring a student at Oxford University to assemble a cryostatic receiver for Guinevere.

Using a network of antennas will enable scientists to reduce noise from local interference in the atmosphere by combining their signals. This amplifies the signals they all receive from deep space, while cutting the relative impact of local noise. It also greatly increases angular resolution, allowing faraway objects to be separated, through a baseline hundreds of miles wide.

Goonhilly's location, less than a degree of longitude away from NASA's Deep Space Network dish site in Madrid, means it can also act as an alternative to the Spanish site, and - at 50 degrees north of the equator - it is within the orbital inclination of the International Space Station. This gives Goonhilly frequent long-duration passes from such objects, allowing plenty of data to be downloaded. "We are just at a very fortuitous location," says Jones.

Goonhilly also provides tracking and telemetry services for satellites and other earth stations. A half-a-billion dollar satellite on the fritz, with its powerful focused antennas off-target, has to rely on a low-power omnidirectional one to receive instructions to put it back on the straight and narrow. "The legacy large antennas are really good for this," says Jones. It can also use its established calibrations to help other earth stations verify and test their antennas.

Finally, although this is something for the future, Jones thinks there is potential to communicate with vehicles in deep space. Noting India's recent Mars probe, which it sent at a fraction of the price of previous missions, he says national agencies are starting to explore austerity in space. "The space agencies realise they can outsource," he says, with Nasa having commissioned SpaceX to build a transporter.

Jones hopes that Goonhilly's visitor centre, once a mainstay of Cornish tourism, will reopen by 2016, although educational outreach work should precede this. The centre will show off Arthur and focus on space travel, with a planetarium and a simulated planetary surface, rather than dwell on its past in the hands of certain British telecommunications company. "It's going to become a really fantastic, inspiring location for people to come," Jones says.

It's time for a tour, laid on by Jones especially for *El Reg*. Currently, the only way around Arthur is by riding a Segway on a course set up next to the dish. We start in the building at the side of the control centre; climbing up a staircase you emerge on a viewing platform for visitors taking the bus-ride around the site.

Here sits an Asus PC connected to a dongle, in turn connected to a simple radio mast, four bars of metal connected at right angles on top of the control centre's roof. This is AmSatUK's tracking station for FUNcube, a UK-Dutch amateur project which has involved launching two miniature satellites for use by schoolchildren.

Out on the plateau, Goonhilly looks little changed from what I saw a decade ago in the BT days, with many signs still using the telco's old corporate font. But Jones does point out some differences, though. Goonhilly has said goodbye to a series of smaller dishes - Gareth, Gawain, Geraint, Galahad - built in the 1980s and 1990s for Inmarsat maritime services. However, satellite data operator Avanti has leased this part of the site and placed new antennas there, along with a sister site near Land's End, a few miles west.

Also gone is Tristan, built in the 1980s for TV services, and Uther, one of the station's oldest and largest dishes at 89.8ft (27.4m) diameter, built in 1968. Pad 2, the concrete base with cut-off cables on which Uther used to sit, has a rather desolate feel to it.

But the edge of Pad 2 is home to a new Goonhilly dish, set up for Californian satellite imaging start-up Planet Labs to communicate with its dozens of "doves": small, cheap satellites launched from the ISS. Just a couple of metres across and within a white radome to protect it from the weather, the dish represents a welcome addition to Goonhilly's new work. "This is part of the business we hadn't envisaged, tracking low-orbit satellites," says Jones.

Innovative private-sector space work looks set to be a major part of its future. It has bought eight new antennas this year, mainly small ones, but also a yet-to-be assembled 16-metre dish, which may take the place of Tristan or Uther.

Elsewhere, several of Goonhilly's remaining big dishes are being renovated. When I visited, the site's most elegant dish, Guinevere – 97ft (29.6m) in diameter, built in 1972 and a relatively light 356 tons (361,713kg) – was undergoing a much-needed clean, with a small patch of white surrounded by a palette of grunge, in advance of joining Arthur in the e-Merlin interferometer network.

Nearby, is Goonhilly's largest dish: Goonhilly 6, also known as Merlin, 104.9ft (32m) in diameter and as a result of being built from aluminium weighing in at just 395 tons (401,339kg). Merlin was built in 1985 by the newly-privatised BT and still uses its original equipment, although Jones says this may be replaced. For now, the metal rows of hardware give it the feel of Dr Evil's computer centre.

But its first use was for the opposite of supervillainry. On 13 July 1985, just 22 years and two days after Telstar's first broadcast, Merlin relayed the *Live Aid* concert from Wembley Stadium to 100 countries around the world. It used to sport a giant *Blue Peter* badge, awarded by the public-spirited BBC children's programme of the same name. While this was present when your correspondent visited the visitor centre in 2004, it has since vanished.

Although it is not part of the e-Merlin work, Merlin will also be converted for deep space work, and GES has already been in discussions with the UK Met Office and the US National Oceanic and Atmospheric Administration. Like the other big dishes, Merlin may no longer be needed for calling out around the world, so it will focus on connecting the earth to the Universe.
If you're tempted by the prospect of mastering a Segway – or if you can

wangle an official or educational visit – then a trip to Goonhilly even before the new centre opens, is worth it.

It should be said, this is a remote spot. Chances are you'll be in the area as part of a trip, unless – of course – you already are local. Britain's surf capital Newquay is about an hour's drive away to the north and is under consideration by the UK Space Agency as a space port. Marazion, home to St Michael's Mount, is half an hour to the west and Penzance forty minutes, while to the north east by half an hour is the historic naval town of Falmouth. There are plenty of places to stay in these towns and in the more remote parts between them and Goonhilly.

The Lizard itself features Flambards theme park, the Cornish Seal Sanctuary at Gweek and Roskilly's farm, which serves ice-cream and more substantial meals.

Nestled on an area of outstanding natural beauty, the huge metal structures look every bit like remnants of the first space age. If you make the trip, however, you won't help but be inspired to see them being repurposed to serve a new era of space exploration.

GPS
50.03, -5.17

Postcode
TR12 6LQ

Getting there
Car: from most of the UK, drive south-west along the M5 and A30, then head south on the A39 and A394 through Truro and past Falmouth. At Helston, turn south on the A3083 for the Lizard past RAF Culdrose, before taking the B3293 east for Coverack. Look out for the big dishes and the BT-branded gatehouse. Public transport: mainline train to Truro, then First's 36 bus runs from the city's bus station to Goonhilly three times a day Monday to Saturday, taking about 95 minutes.

Entry
Goonhilly Earth Station is not currently open to the public, although it plans to reopen its visitor centre by 2016 (check website below for updates).

Online resources
www.goonhilly.org/
www.cornwallsegway.co.uk/tours.php

The Lizard Wireless Station, Marconi Centre and Wireless Field
Cornwall

SA Mathieson

GEEK'S
GUIDE
TO BRITAIN

Marconi: the west of England's very own Italian wireless pioneer

A trip to the Lizard King's monument

This is the story of a 22-year-old technology genius, who, stung by the lack of interest in his work in his homeland, moved to a new country to develop his ideas.

In a single year, this individual extended the performance of a key technology of his time by a factor of more than 20.

It sounds like an outlandish tale even by Silicon Valley standards, but by the end of 1901, Guglielmo Marconi had pushed the range of wireless communications from just over 80 miles (128km) to 2,000 (3,220km).

His breakthrough turned convention about the then-new wireless technology on its head, earning him a joint Nobel Prize for Physics nine years later.

If one technology dominated the early 20th century, it was wireless – thanks largely to Marconi. Before TV, Marconi's work established wireless as the world's first mass medium, trouncing telegraph and rubbishing print.

He facilitated the spread of communications, entertainment, politics and propaganda around the globe in a fast-modernising world of motor-driven cars, and propeller-powered aircraft.

Long-range wireless transmissions made the oceans a safer place, too, allowing ships to stay in touch with the land long after they had journeyed over the horizon. Marconi's work also allowed the development of the SOS signal – and his company received the first one in 1910.

The birthplace of long-range wireless is an area surrounded by ocean, so remote it feels like the edge of the world: Cornwall's Lizard peninsula, the southernmost part of Great Britain.

From a pair of sites – a hut on the coast near The Lizard village then a purpose-built facility near the village of Poldhu – Marconi worked on the generation and transmission of wireless radio signals.

You can visit the scene of Marconi's endeavours today.

Assuming you are already in the area, you can visit both in an afternoon by car or bus. As it generally opens and closes first, it makes sense to follow Marconi and start at Lizard Wireless Station. After half a mile's easy walk from the village along the Lloyds Lane track, you meet the coast path with views of cliffs, a nearby lighthouse and, of course, the sea.

Built in 1900, this Grade II-listed building is the world's oldest surviving Marconi wireless station and is run by the National Trust. It was from here that Marconi conducted his early work, reaching out across the sea.

Of course, Marconi didn't invent wireless; it owes its origins to German physicist Heinrich Hertz. Marconi, the son of a wealthy landowner and a member of Ireland's Jameson spirit distilling family, had studied at the Livorno Technical Institute and University of Bologna. He became interested in Hertz's work and by 1895 had extended the range of wireless to 1.5 miles (2.5km).

But the Italian government wasn't interested, so Marconi moved to Britain – a canny move given its erstwhile status as ruler of the world's waves. He gained a patent, along with interest from the military, the Post Office and the Lloyd's of London insurance market.

As the main use for wireless seemed to be at sea, Marconi and his backers decided to move their operations to Britain's coast, with sites that would reach shipping lanes as far as possible across the Atlantic.

South west Cornwall was the obvious choice and in summer 1900, Marconi chose his site at Lizard village – at Bass Point, near Lizard Point, the most southerly point of the Lizard peninsula – and a second location a little further up the coast at Poldhu, on the peninsula's western side.

At Bass Point he moved a shed previously used as a waiting room for a carriage service to Helston train station near to the edge of the cliffs, and kitted it out as both a ship-to-shore station and an experimental base. The site was already well connected, just a few hundred yards from a Lloyd's signal station built in 1872 (now a private residence), used for flag communications with passing boats.

Marconi extended the range of wireless to 32 miles (51.4km), enough to cross the English Channel. But although some naval tests saw signals reaching as far as 88 miles (142km), many scientists thought stations needed a clear line of sight to communicate. It was Marconi who disproved this.

Marconi formed the Wireless Telegraph and Signal Company in 1897, which became the Marconi's Wireless Telegraph Company in 1900, and the Lizard hut was opened on 18 January 1901. On 23 January, the day after Queen Victoria's death, Marconi received an S signal in Morse code from another of his firm's stations on the Isle of Wight, 186 miles (300km) to the east and well beyond the optical reach of the two stations.

Although no one was sure how, he had shown that radio signals could travel hundreds of miles.

The restored shed is a low wooden structure with a cracking sea view. It's here I meet David Barlow, its volunteer warden and a former merchant marine radio officer. "I suppose I have to mention the horrible word – cable," he says, of wireless's rival technology. The signal station had a private telegraph link to London and was installing submarine cable to Bilbao in Spain.

Visit today and you'll find that the main room has been equipped to look like it did when first in use, based on a photo from 1903. Wardens take delight in demonstrating the 16,000-volt spark transmitter: Barlow checks first to see if anyone has a pacemaker, which can be disrupted by the equipment, then fires it up, its sparks producing a loud snapping.

The desk also features the glass-jar batteries, an analogue clock and Morse equipment, below a framed painting of the St Louis – a passenger ship overdue in Britain by many days, whose near-arrival was first reported by a ship with radio to this station in 1903.

The St Louis is not the only boat that had cause to be grateful to this station. In 1906, the Berlin Convention established "SOS" as the international distress signal and on 18 April 1910, the station received what is thought to be the first.

The cargo ship SS Minnehaha had run aground on rocks in the Isles of Scilly, on its way in from New York. Its passengers and crew were rescued by locals, but wireless meant that the ship was able to stay in touch with the mainland.

The next room houses modern radio equipment, which can be used by licensed amateur operators who appreciate a nice sea view and a long heritage. When I visited, radio fan Malcolm Bolton was using the set.

Having successfully communicated with a station in Australia, he was using an Android app to turn an audio signal back into a television picture from Germany. "It's like electronic fly-fishing," he said, seeking the right conditions to bounce signals off the ionosphere right around the planet – which is how Marconi's signals were reaching so far.

The next chapter in the story carries on five miles north west of the wireless hut, as Marconi looked to send radio waves across the Atlantic. He purchased a plot of land just south of Poldhu Cove, and built a signal station that opened in 1901, next to a then recently-built hotel (now a nursing home).

Wireless Field today, with the Marconi Centre and former hotel behind
Photo: SA Mathieson

This initially consisted of a circle of 20 masts, each 200 feet (60.9m) high, connected to a 25 kilowatt transmitter capable of producing a spark audible a mile away. The buildings housed research, signal transmission and power generation.

In June 1901, Poldhu communicated with a station at Crookhaven in County Cork, 225 miles away. In September, high winds blew down the masts, but that wasn't going to stop Marconi making history. With a temporary pair of 160-foot masts he set off for Newfoundland in Canada to receive transmission of the first transatlantic wireless signal – from those masts.

On 9 December, he used cable telegraphy to ask his team to start sending signals. On 12 December 1901, he heard their reply: a series of taps in Morse code for the letter "S." Wireless radio communications had crossed the Atlantic, and further tests found that Poldhu's range could exceed 2,000 miles.

January 1903 saw the first transmission from the US, from American President Theodore Roosevelt to King Edward VII. This may have been the first example of poorly timed international calls due to time differences; Poldhu received the message at night, after the post office in the nearby village of Mullion had closed, so it didn't get through to the king until the next morning.

This didn't put off the Prince and Princess of Wales – later King George V and Queen Mary – visiting both Poldhu and The Lizard stations that July, providing some amusing anecdotes (the brakes on Marconi's car failed going down a hill; rather than overtake the royals and break with protocol, the driver steered into a wall) and many of the surviving photographs of both stations.

Marconi eventually moved the wireless telegraphy work to new purpose-built stations in Ireland and Canada, with great commercial success. Cable companies charged a shilling a word: "Marconi charged sixpence, and really cleaned up," Keith Matthew, honorary secretary of the Poldhu Amateur Radio Club, told *The Register* on our trip around the sites.

Poldhu continued with maritime communications, in 1904 launching Ocean News, a daily news bulletin for liner passengers. As signals didn't always reach across the ocean, boats within range would retransmit it. One night in April 1912, it is thought that the *SS Minnehaha* – the sender of the first SOS – retransmitted the bulletin to the world's biggest liner, sailing across the Atlantic on its maiden voyage; yes, that would be the Titanic.

Poldhu was run by the government during World War I, communicating with ships and submarines. Afterwards, when it reverted to Marconi, it developed transatlantic wireless telephony, introduced in 1920, and Charles Franklin developed directional short-wave beam technology – as well as coaxial cable, to get power to the transmitters across the field.

However, the site was remote and expensive to use. Marconi considered moving a few miles east to Goonhilly, which half a century later would host its own transatlantic breakthrough, but instead the firm set up its Empire Wireless Beam station at Bodmin in central Cornwall, although that site has since been demolished to upgrade the A30 main road.

Poldhu was to share the same fate, minus dual carriageway: it was closed in 1934, with the land donated to the National Trust – on the condition it was cleared.

The clearance wasn't quite finished; what remains today is a series of building foundations and tile floors picked out by encroaching grass and other assorted flora, holes and trenches. Britain has far better preserved Roman villas.

There is a monument to Marconi and his colleagues on the coast path just outside the field, a column near the edge of the land that looks a little like the beacons that were used to communicate before cables and wireless. Put up after the National Trust took over the land, its plaques record the achievements of Marconi, Franklin, the station's designer John Fleming and their colleagues. But for many years, that was it.

However, 2001 saw an attempt to reclaim Marconi's site from history, with the Marconi Centre. It's an unassuming barn-like building that opened in 2001 on the centenary of that transatlantic transmission.

The centre was partly funded by the former Marconi PLC (during a brief period of corporate independence and brand awareness raising before largely being swallowed by Ericsson in 2006), the National Trust and Poldhu Amateur Radio Club, who put in a total of £311,913, with a final £141,913 from the European Regional Development Fund.

The centre tells Marconi's story through a short film, a set of display panels and some interesting artefacts. It also includes three well-appointed radio rooms, used by the Poldhu Amateur Radio Club – who staff the centre – and visiting licensed operators.

Both Poldhu and the Lizard wireless hut are in lovely coastal locations, although if you're travelling with those unaccountably less than enthralled by the early history of wireless telecommunications you might drop them off at amusement park Flambards, the Cornish Seal Sanctuary at Gweek or the small seaside resort Coverack, all on the Lizard peninsula.

For catering, Roskilly's Farm, which produces the ice-cream of the same name, is free to visit and serves food all day. If you want to linger, you can even stay in the cottage attached to the Lizard Wireless Hut, courtesy of the National Trust.

If time is short, or the buildings are closed, you can still leave the uninterested on Poldhu beach, and walk up to and across Wireless Field. With its mysterious ruins and earthworks, it feels like the site of a lost civilisation – rather than a field on the edge of Britain which sent a signal to an Italian in Canada and shrank the world.

It's a remote but profound place; much of what made it important has vanished. Radio signals, like the buildings and aerials once at Poldhu, are ephemeral.

However, because of what happened here we are swimming in such signals and surrounded by the technology they allow. To adapt Sir Christopher Wren's memorial in St Paul's Cathedral: if you seek Guglielmo Marconi's memorial, look around you.

GPS
Lizard Station
49.963771, -5.2187740 (for the Lizard Village's post office)

Postcode
TR12 7NQ

Getting there
By car: A30, south on the A39 and A394, south at Helston on A3083 (becomes the A3033), park at The Lizard Village. Walk east through the village and take Lloyds Lane to the coast path; the station is just to the west. Alternatively, park in the National Trust car park at Lizard Lighthouse and walk east along the coast path to the station. Public transport: train to Redruth, First's 37 bus from the train station to The Lizard.

Entry
No fee, but a £1 donation is requested. Station is open April-September on Sundays, Tuesdays, Wednesdays, Thursdays and Fridays 1-3pm, shorter hours in winter, and only in reasonable weather. Check the website for details, or contact the National Trust office on 01326 561407.

Online resources
http://lizardwireless.org/

GPS
The Marconi Centre and Wireless Field
50.030489, -5.263368

Postcode
TR12 7JB

Getting there
Car: as above to the A3083. Shortly after passing the southern end of RNAS Culdrose, turn right for Poldhu Cove. At the end of the beach after a bridge, turn right up a private road for Poldhu Nursing Home. Look for the Marconi Centre car-park on the left. Public transport: same as above; Poldhu is on the 37 bus route, about 65 minutes from Redruth and 20 minutes from The Lizard.

Entry
There is no charge for entry, but donations are gratefully received. The station is normally open for a few hours on Sunday afternoons and Tuesday and Friday evenings all year, Wednesday afternoons from May to September and Thursday afternoons in July and August. Exact times can be found on the website. Wireless Field and the Marconi monument are open at any time.

Amateur licence holders wishing to operate radio station GB2GM are welcome, as are groups, but are asked to book in advance.

Online resources
www.marconi-centre-poldhu.org.uk

James Clerk Maxwell House and Foundation
Edinburgh

Bill Ray

Saturn's rings, radio waves ... poetry? At home with Scotland's Mr Physics

James Clerk Maxwell's house

Say the word "radio" and the mind goes to Guglielmo Marconi, the Italian emigrant whose work on the watershed of Cornwall and the Atlantic Ocean helped turn wireless into the defining medium of the early 20th century.

But radio wasn't invented by Marconi – or any one person. Rather, it was discovered, and the man who drove that discovery was James Clerk Maxwell.

Maxwell is essential to physics as we understand it today. He didn't invent radio waves, but he did posit their existence. Without that leap of logic we wouldn't be wandering through the electro-smog in which we now delight.

Yet Maxwell's contributions are not confined to radio: his theories on the rings of Saturn were borne out by 20th century science; he produced the first colour photo; and he founded and helped build Cambridge University's Cavendish Laboratory in 1879 where he was the inaugural Cavendish Professor of Physics. The laboratory has since produced 29 Nobel Prize winners.

Oh, and he was a poet, too. This was the 1800s, after all, when a chap with a beard could really make something of himself.

Maxwell's birthplace and early home was a terraced house in Edinburgh New Town, built for his father in 1820. New Town is a marvel of 19th century civic thinking, designed to alleviate overcrowding, that marries space with elegant architecture.

These days Maxwell's house belongs to the James Clerk Maxwell Foundation, which managed to buy it in 1993. If you want to see the house in person then you'll have to make an appointment, but there's a virtual tour and those interested in learning more about James Maxwell can take an Edinburgh walking tour covering his life.

Maxwell was born at 14 India Street on 31 July, 1831, though he only lived there for a couple of years before his family relocated to their 1,500-acre country estate in Galloway. When he was 10 he moved back to attend the Edinburgh Academy but lived with his aunt, who resided around the corner from the Maxwell family home – which was, at that point, being let out. In fact, 14 India Street was let to a succession of tenants; Maxwell inherited it on his father's death but never lived there again. He went on to study physics at Edinburgh and then at Cambridge University.

In 1977 the James Clerk Maxwell Foundation was established to remind the world just what a marvellous chap he was, and in 1993 the opportunity arose to acquire the house in which he was born. That acquisition was largely made possible thanks to one Sydney Ross, who was relocating to the US and took the opportunity to leave some money behind – but it also owed much to the increasing use of email, which had devalued local properties.

Being situated about a 30-minute stroll from the courts, the houses had attracted lawyers, whose briefs were delivered by hand. Email enabled them to move further away and so burst a minor property bubble. Professor David Ritchie, director of the James Clerk Maxwell Foundation, was then able to move in and grab the place for the nation.

If you want to look around the house then you need to get in touch with the James Clerk Maxwell Foundation, who will fix a time and day for Professor Ritchie to show you around.

Once bought, the house had to be extensively restored to a state Maxwell would recognise: the dark colours of the late Victorian era were reinstated and door frames returned to their former glory, and various sponsors and donors stumped up the cash to make the place look respectable while others contributed art and objects to furnish a small museum.

Maxwell might be best known for his equations covering the behaviour of an electromagnetic charge – but that was by no means his only contribution to the world. In the dining room we can see the world's first colour photograph. Maxwell set out to prove that three pictures shot through different filters could be combined to create a single image. The image of a tartan ribbon wasn't perfect, but it did work, and thus set in stone the concept of "RGB" – red, green and blue – with which we're so familiar today.

Maxwell is most often pictured holding a colour wheel, a disk of card with sections of different colours that can be spun to create white. It seems obvious now, but at the time this was a significant breakthrough, and various versions of the disk are scattered around the room.

We can also see his first presented paper, on the rendering of mathematically correct ovals, written in his own hand. This was presented to the Royal Society of Edinburgh in 1846, but not by Maxwell who (at 14) was considered too young to be standing in front of such an august audience.

He was 26 when he proved, mathematically, that the rings of Saturn could be neither solid nor made of liquid. The only form that would allow stable rotation was a collection of small rocks, which from Earth assumed the form of a solid ring.

Yet the breakthrough for which he is best known is linking light to electromagnetism, and we can see his presentation on that subject too. The breakthrough was his measurement of the speed of electromagnetism, which came too close to the speed of light to be coincidental, leading to the inevitable conclusion that the two things were one and the same.

According to Maxwell: "The velocity of transverse undulations in our hypothetical medium... agrees so exactly with the velocity of light... that we can scarcely avoid the inference that light consists in the transverse undulations of the same medium which is the cause of electric and magnetic phenomena."

From there we have the electromagnetic spectrum, and radio waves, and everything else. Maxwell fits squarely between Sir Isaac Newton and Albert Einstein, and deserves to be as well known as either of them.

It would be years before the implications of his discovery would be understood, and he spent the next few decades refining it. It was more than a century before the Voyager spacecraft confirmed his proof about the rings of Saturn, and we're still sorting out whether his electromagnetic phenomena are particles or waves (spoiler: they're both), so this was a man well ahead of his time.

But mathematicians can do that: while physicists have to spend billions building colliders, and chemists obtain rare samples to feed their alchemy, the mathematician can predict how things have to be. Maxwell was a poet, and as one of his many works explains:

Of the Philosophic Spirit

Richly may my son inherit;

As for Poetry, inter it

With the myths of other days.

Cut the thing entirely, lest yon

College Don should put the question,

Why not stick to what you're best on?

Mathematics always pays.

Not that he had any sons, or daughters. Denied permission to marry his first cousin he ended up with the boss's (the principal's) daughter while at Marischal College, Aberdeen. Katherine Dewar was, by all accounts, a devoted wife who helped him with his experiments, but the couple didn't reproduce.

Maxwell himself was almost certainly born in the upstairs bedroom at 14 India Street, now known as the "Motorola Room". The room is largely devoid of furniture now but would have been the master bedroom when the house was occupied by John Clerk Maxwell and his wife.

In keeping with the fashion of the time the bedroom has double doors into an upstairs drawing room, now available for scientific seminars and the like. When guests were expected the bed could be packed away and the doors, which are decorated with eagles to celebrate the victory at Waterloo, would be opened to create a single room.

The next floor isn't open to visitors as it's rented to an HR outsourcing company. The stairs are flanked with engravings of the scientists onto whose shoulders Maxwell climbed.

Beyond the house itself there is the walking tour, which doesn't start at his place of birth but at St John's Church where the family spent their Sunday afternoons. Behind the church there's a small parade of socially idealistic shops and a cheerful rustic cafe supplying victuals to those tracing the route.

The James Clerk Maxwell Foundation provides a PDF with a map and description of the three-mile walk, which includes various sites associated with the great man. There is also a smartphone app, which comes with a quiz and directions, but as the directions seemed inadequate and the quiz answers didn't match information on the foundation's own website, we decided to stick with a print out.

That route took us past 14 India Street and on to 31 Heriot Row, from where James Clerk Maxwell's aunt sent him off to school dressed as a country bumpkin, much to the amusement of the other pupils who wasted no time in labelling him "dafty" - which doesn't seem to have bothered him as much as it might have. The last laugh goes to Maxwell, as in 2006 the school spent £4.6m building the impressive James Clerk Maxwell Science Centre, where those who can afford it can get a decent education.

Other than that additional building the school remains surprisingly unchanged, from the front at least, which makes sense given its continuing mission to educate the gentry of Scotland's capital city.

From the school it's a bit of a climb back to Heriot Row, but fortunately there's Clark's Bar on the way. The pub opened 20 years after Maxwell died, and although it's spelt differently, the call of a decent pint is enough to smooth over a few historical anomalies.

From there we continue up to George Street, where a statue of the great man stands (or, rather, sits) looking down the road. Clasped in his hands is the colour wheel that could be spun to demonstrate how white light is a combination of everything else, while beneath him sits Toby – the dog with whom Maxwell shared so many of his ideas before testing them on humans.

The statue is impressive, though his equations are relegated to a small plate on the back, and the friezes that adorn the sides are a little impenetrable without footnotes.

That's Apollo on the left, representing light. He's been shot by Eros, who's representing gravity, which is why he's smaller than the others (gravity being the weakest force, though still able to influence light). The chap holding the rubber sheet is a suspiciously Greek-looking Einstein showing off his theory of relativity, while the beggar represents the end of classical science and the warrior relaxes as the battle is done.

Einstein might not have favoured the toga in real life but he was a big fan of James Clerk Maxwell. According to the man himself: "The special theory of relativity owes its origins to Maxwell's equations of the electromagnetic field."

Visiting the house is a great experience, though perhaps best suited to the more dedicated fan (or group) who can make forward arrangements. To see the notebooks and tools used by the man himself is an inspiration, and scientific groups in Edinburgh should certainly consider the seminar room for meetings or talks.

The walking tour is fun, taking you through Edinburgh's (New Town) residential areas which might not be part of the usual tourist trail. The Royal Society of Edinburgh's impressive home might now be a Lakeland store (the society has moved up the road), but walking around the route one gets a feel for how the city once was, and how James Clerk Maxwell would have known it.

If you've an hour or two to kill in Edinburgh then take the walking tour. If you're a physicist who wants to know more about how physics came to be then get a couple of similarly minded mates together and make an appointment to see the house where so much of it started.

GPS
55.955279, -3.205601

Post code
EH3 6EZ

Getting there
14 India Street is a 20-minute walk from Edinburgh Waverley station. Go west along Princes Street then turn right onto Castle Street crossing George Street and Queen Street to turn left onto Heriot Row and then India Street is on the right. A stone plaque marks the wall of number 14.

The walking tour starts at St John's Church, which can be found by emerging from Edinburgh Waverley station and taking a left to walk east along Princes Street for just under a mile, when the church will be visible on the left.

Entry
There is no charge for viewing the house, but an appointment must be made with the James Clerk Maxwell Foundation

Other resources
www.clerkmaxwellfoundation.org/

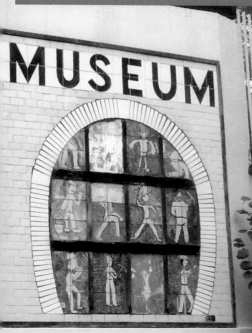

Brunel Museum
London

Brid-Aine Parnell

Bridge, ship ' n' tunnel – the Brunels' hidden Thames trip

Monument to a trio who left their mark on Blighty

When you mention Brunel to most people, they think of the one with the funny name – Isambard Kingdom Brunel. A few folks will know that his father Marc Isambard Brunel was the first famous engineering Brunel, but not many will know that Isambard's own son, Henry Marc Brunel, was also an engineer and finished some of Isambard's projects after his death.

Between the three of them, the Brunels created landmarks all over the UK; perhaps most famously the Clifton Suspension Bridge which spans the Avon Gorge, linking Clifton in Bristol to Leigh Woods in Somerset.

That bridge, which Isambard Kingdom Brunel designed and often called his "first child," wasn't actually completed until after his death and only came about at all because Isambard was nearly drowned in an accident at the massive project he was working on in London with his father: the Thames Tunnel.

It is this masterpiece of engineering, which invented new methods of tunnelling underground and is why the Brunels are credited with creating underground transportation – and by extension, the modern city itself – that you see if you go along to the Brunel Museum in Rotherhithe, London.

The museum itself is in Marc Brunel's Engine House, built in 1842 - the year before the Thames Tunnel was opened – to house the engines that pumped to keep the Tunnel dry. A small exhibition tells the story of the design and construction of the 1,299ft (396m)-long tunnel, the first to have been successfully built underneath a navigable river. The display panels also detail the innovative tunnelling shield technique invented by Marc and Isambard that's still used to build tunnels today, although these days it's machines doing the hard work instead of men. Back then, labourers would spend two hours at a time digging, often while also being gassed and showered with shit.

The River Thames at that time was the sewer of London and the tunnel was constantly waterlogged, leading to a build-up of effluent and methane gas. The result was that not only would miners pass out from the gas – even if they didn't, men who re-surfaced were left senseless after their two-hour shift – but there were also explosions as the gas was set alight by the miners' candles.

Although it's a tidy and well-kept little exhibition, it is not really why you come to the museum. You come for its underground chamber, which was only opened up to the public in 2010 after 150 years of being closed off by the London transportation system. This is the Grand Entrance Hall to the Thames Tunnel, used in Brunel's day as a concert hall and fairground and now in the process of being turned into a permanent exhibition.

As Transport for London was building the new Overground lines, it agreed to pour a concrete floor about halfway up the Grand Entrance Hall, giving the museum the top part of the Hall while trains run below. While the museum is working on turning it into something more permanent, you can get a guided tour through a very small four-foot entrance and down some scaffolding to stand in a room that no one has been in for more than 100 years. The new human-size doorway, staircase and gallery were due to open in January 2016, courtesy of an Association of Independent Museums' Biffa Grant.

Once renovations are completed, concerts and other events will be held in the underground chamber, whose walls are still lined with the soot of old trains and carry the marks of the sweeping wooden staircases that once led people down into the tunnel.

Originally intended as a means of getting cargo across what was then a hugely trafficked river, the Thames Tunnel ran out of money before it was able to build the extended entrance necessary to get horses and carts underground. Instead, the tunnel was opened for pedestrian use in 1843. It quickly became a major tourist attraction, with two million people a year paying a penny to walk through.

It sounds successful but folks were also paying a penny to use any of the other ways to cross the Thames. Being new and daring, the tunnel was seen as pretty scary. To try to generate more payback for the massive investment, the tunnel opened up some of the very first tourist tat shops, selling Thames Tunnel souvenirs including cups and plates – so you could prove you were brave enough not only to walk the tunnel, but to stop and browse along the way.

However, as time went on, the seedier side of Victorian London started to reckon a dark, underground tunnel might be the perfect place to conduct some nefarious business and the numbers of respectable tourists declined. Various projects to make more money out of it were tried, including turning it into what must have been a fantastical subterranean fairground to attract even more visitors, before it was sold to the East London Railway Company in 1865. A part of the original tunnel is still visible today if you peer down the line from Wapping station towards Rotherhithe.

Although it was a financial disaster, the tunnel was a marvel of engineering and made underground transportation around the world a possibility, all because of the tunnel shielding method invented by Marc Brunel.

Before his innovation, tunnels had been attempted twice beneath the Thames, but had failed because of the soft clay, quicksand and flooding that collapsed the efforts. The tunnelling shield was a sort of cage structure that was pushed to the front of the tunnel. In the original design, men in the cages would dig forward a little, while those behind were shoring up the tunnel by building its walls. The design was later improved by engineers working for the railway companies building the London Underground and still forms the basic idea behind modern tunnel boring machines.

Despite the vast improvement in methodology, digging the Thames Tunnel was still a dangerous job; one in which Isambard himself, working as an engineer for his father, nearly died. He was the only survivor of the second major flood of the tunnel in 1828, when six men died. Half-drowned, he was sent to Bristol to convalesce and here he designed his first individual project, the Clifton Suspension Bridge. Although it's the most famous of his bridges, it's by no means the only one that Isambard designed, which you'll learn if you take the Museum's boat tour of London, which finishes in the Grand Entrance Hall underground chamber.

The boat tour starts at Embankment Tube Station. Be prepared, though – the tour is long and if you're going to do it in the depths of winter, or you're not the type that can skip a meal, you should fuel-up before you set off. You take the ordinary Thames Clipper ferry (at a 40 percent discount) with your enthusiastic guide, the museum director Robert Hulse.

He points out the remains of Isambard Brunel's Hungerford Suspension footbridge, since replaced by the railway bridge for Charing Cross Station and the Golden Jubilee footbridges, with the suspension chains carted off for use on the Clifton Suspension Bridge. But he'll also point out that Tower Bridge – arguably London's most famous – and the Blackfriars Railway Bridge were designed by Sir John Wolfe-Barry, whose partner for many years was Henry Marc Brunel. Brunel worked on Tower Bridge and helped design Blackfriars Railway Bridge, which is now the world's largest solar-powered bridge, and home to Blackfriars station.

Museum pump house, with cafe
Photo: Gavin Clarke

There's just time for a quick (and the only) toilet break before you get off the boat at Masthouse Terrace, Isle of Dogs to visit the site where Isambard built and very slowly launched the biggest ship of its time, the *SS Great Eastern*. The colossal iron sailing and steam ship was by far the largest ever built: it was so huge that people in some ports in Asia apparently ran away when they saw it.

The ill-fated ship was another Brunel technical masterpiece and another financial disaster, failing to live up to its considerable potential. The ship seemed doomed from the start, with its long – and boring for spectators – sideways launch and the collapse of its engineer just afterwards. Isambard Kingdom Brunel suffered a stroke and died ten days later at the age of 53.

Money problems dogged the construction of the *Great Eastern*, which Isambard took on after his success with pioneering steam travel to North America on the *SS Great Western* and *SS Great Britain*. The *Great Eastern* was intended for longer voyages as far as Australia, and because coal had not yet been discovered on the continent, it was built to carry all the coal it would need for a round trip from Britain. The ship was powered and manoeuvred by single screw propulsion and paddle wheels, along with auxiliary sails.

Brunel reckoned he would need around £500,000 to build the ship, but the naval architect and shipbuilder John Scott Russell tendered only £377,200 for the project, which Isambard accepted. Because of the size of the finished ship, it had to be built sideways to the Thames and Brunel was planning a mechanical slip to get it into the water. However, Scott Russell went bankrupt, leaving the Eastern Company to finish the ship, despite the fact that three-quarters of the hull hadn't been finished and there were 1,200 tons of iron missing.

Brunel agreed to launch the ship in November 1857, although he wanted to spend longer on her. He wanted a quiet launch, explaining that the sideways slip would be boring for spectators. He was horrified to discover that Eastern Company directors had sold 3,000 tickets for the launch and others who heard about it swarmed the area seeking vantage points from which to watch.

The first launch failed because the steam winches and manual capstans being used to haul the mammoth craft, nicknamed Leviathan, weren't enough. The ship eventually managed to get into the water at the end of January the following year, after hydraulic rams were brought in.

The *Great Eastern* was in the water, but it still had to be fitted out and it was now the Eastern Company's turn to be approaching bankruptcy. The directors quickly formed a new company, the Great Ship Company, and bought the ship for peanuts so as to have enough money left over to finish her. Finally, she set out on her maiden voyage at the end of 1859 but only made it as far as Hastings before there was a huge explosion, killing five stokers with superheated steam and injuring others. The accident was caused by a closed steam exhaust pipe, but luckily the ship's strong bulkheads contained the explosion.

This wasn't the only piece of bad luck the ship was to have, however. It had been built for trade and transport to Australia and the Far East, but its owners didn't believe there was enough trade to send her that far. So the *Great Eastern* only ever sailed the Atlantic. The economies of scale and efficiencies Brunel worked out were for long trips around the world – as a transatlantic steamer, the *Great Eastern* just wasn't worth its investment.

The ship was eventually broken up in 1890 and it was the *Great Britain*– also designed by Brunel and the first iron steamer to cross the Atlantic – that survived to become a tourist attraction in Bristol.

After a walk along the river with a view towards Greenwich, the tour hops on the DLR and Overground lines to get to the Museum and the underground chamber, including a quick stop at Wapping to look down the original section of Thames Tunnel. Hulse will proudly tell you as you exit at Rotherhithe that the Brunels' Thames Tunnel is the oldest section of the oldest underground network in the world and without it, modern cities would not be possible.

The tour ends with a nice frisson of excitement in the underground chamber with the tale of how Isambard Kindgom Brunel – voted second only to Winston Churchill in a BBC TV poll of the British public to find the 100 Greatest Britons – nearly drowned. The museum is worth a wander around, but the cafe isn't really worthy of the name, consisting mainly of a chap with a kettle although cakes have been introduced. However, Hulse may tell you he's off to lunch at the nearby Mayflower, the oldest pub on the River Thames, where Brunel himself once supped, and you're welcome to join him.

If you'd rather not, there's the Old Salt Quay pub a little further along the river, or the new Brunel pub on Brunel Road, or you can head towards Canada Water and Surrey Quays station for more pubs and restaurants. This is also, incidentally, one of the places where those in your group who aren't enamoured of engineering prowess can hang out, as there's a cinema here. Otherwise, Greenwich with all its museums and sights is not too far away.

GPS
The Brunel Museum
51.501581, -0.052950

Postcode
SE16 4LF

Getting there
Train: overground to Rotherhithe station, one hundred yards away or the Jubilee Line to Canada Water or Bermondsey for a ten-minute walk. Bus: Nos 381 and C10 stop outside Rotherhithe station, while 1 and 188 stop at Canada Water.

Entry
Open seven days a week 10:00-5:00. Adults £3.00, £1.50 for concessions. Free for children under 16.

Boat tour
Meet at Embankment Tube Station on the Northern, Circle, Bakerloo and District lines, at 10.45am on Tuesdays, Thursdays, Fridays or Saturdays. The guide will be carrying a London Walks pamphlet.

Walking tour
10.45am on Sundays and Mondays and 6.15pm on Wednesdays. From Bermondsey tube station on the Jubilee line.

Online resources
www.brunel-museum.org.uk
www.walks.com/

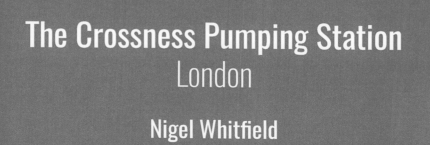

The Crossness Pumping Station
London

Nigel Whitfield

Photo: Nigel Whitfield

Taming the Thames – the place that plugged London's Great Stink

How Joseph Bazalgette flushed the capital into the modern age

At various times in the history of the UK, there's been a massive stink at Westminster, accompanied by demands that "something must be done". We'll be stumbling through the demands for PR after the 2015 election for a while yet, but spare a thought for the politicians of 1858 who had to endure The Great Stink.

With a river soaked in effluent, the stench back then came from outside the House of Commons rather than inside. Cholera raged across London, killing three times as many as in areas with cleaner water. While John Snow had traced an outbreak in Soho to a water pump, many still believed in theories about miasma – that the source of illness was in the air.

Against this background, Joseph Bazalgette was given the go-ahead to build the sewer system that finally made London a really modern city. With a system of interconnecting sewers both north and south of the river connecting to the growing suburbs, the Thames was finally tamed. In fact, the system had been planned four years previously, in response to the cholera crisis, but it was the Great Stink that gave the impetus to pass an enabling Act.

Bazalgette's system is really two separate ones, with the different branches of each converging, before ultimately the sewage was still dumped into the river – just not where it would bother anyone who really mattered. In the north, the sewers converge at Abbey Mills, where a pumping station linked them to the Northern Outfall Sewer. In the south, sewage was originally dumped into Deptford Creek. By 1860 work had begun on the Southern Outfall Sewer, which was to take the waste all the way to Crossness, on the edge of the Thames a little way beyond Woolwich. And in 1865 the Crossness Pumping Station was opened.

At Crossness, a huge covered reservoir stored everything that came from the sewers south of the river. Covering over six acres, and capable of holding 27 million gallons, it was filled by the engines in the pump house raising the sewage up, and then opened at high tide, to allow the contents to flow out to sea as the waters ebbed. In 1865, sewage treatment as we know it hadn't been developed, so the aim was simply to dump the muck as far away from where it mattered as possible.

The Victorians, of course, did things in style. Just as two years before, a banquet had been held at Farringdon Station to mark the opening of the world's first underground railway, so Crossness was opened with pomp and circumstance, with the Prince of Wales starting the engines in the company of two other princes, a Duke and a pair of Archbishops.

As you might expect, given the spirit of the age, the four engines – built by James Watt – were given suitably regal names: Victoria, Prince Consort, Albert Edward and Alexandra. Another four engines were added in 1897 to provide additional capacity. A few years later, the original steam engines were upgraded with additional cylinders, before the four additional engines were replaced by diesel in 1913.

By 1956, all the steam-powered machines had been decommissioned, with the last major use of the Prince Consort engine being to help pump water after the great floods of 1953. Like much old Victorian machinery, their story would have ended with rot and decay, were it not for the Crossness Engines Trust.

In 1985, a group was formed with the aim of preserving the engines and ultimately restoring them. Converted into a Trust to give it legal standing in 1988, it was granted a lease in 1993. The Crossness Trust's aim is to restore the buildings and engines to their 1899 condition and create an exhibition to accompany them. Despite delays, work is proceeding thanks to a grant from the Heritage Lottery Fund, and it's hoped that a new access route to an exhibition – avoiding the still-working sections of the Thames Water plant – due to be complete by 2016.

In the meantime, the engines aren't sitting idle. Prince Consort has been fully restored and work continues on Victoria. At open days several times each year, Prince Consort is steamed and visitors can see the engine in action, as well as admire the interior of the pumping station. I arranged a visit to the site to coincide with a scheduled steaming day to see what's in store for *Register* readers.

On entering, the first thing you'll see is a large space, which at the moment contains a temporary exhibition, as well as a refreshments area. This was part of the boiler house, though it's now an airy space with a few static displays about Bazalgette's sewage system, including a collection of toilets, some small engines and pumps, and a scale model of the building. By the time work is complete, there should be a lot more in the exhibition.

The real centrepieces of any visit, of course, are the engines themselves. As you can see from the photos, much of the Victorian ironwork has been beautifully painted. Considering this was a sewage pumping station, the effort put into its design and building is astonishing – and so too must have been the day-to-day work, keeping brass handrails beautifully polished, as well as tending to the engines.

Entering from the boiler shed, you're actually coming in the back way: the original front entrance now leads to the Triple Expansion shed, the additional building created in 1897. That newer building is largely empty now, with a huge basement where the old pumps used to be, giving a good idea of the scale of things.

Back in the main part of the building, while most of the ironwork in the central section has been restored, a glance around shows that this is still something of a work in progress. The Prince Consort engine is fully restored and working, while Victoria is being worked on. Both engines are at the same end of the building, and the plan is to do most of the work on that side of the engine house, while the other side is largely untouched.

That gives quite a dramatic effect – look one way from the central atrium and you can imagine that little has been touched since the pumps there finally stopped and started to gather rust. Turn through 180 degrees and you'll see vibrant colours, a huge beam engine – sometimes working under steam – and another being restored, as if you've turned not just 180 degrees but back over 100 years.

Looking at all this, one of the things that strikes you is how quickly it was all done, and on what scale. From an enabling bill in 1858, it took just seven years before Crossness started pumping. Bazalgette's system of sewers still forms the backbone of London's waste system 150 years on, when the city is about four times the size it was.

You can't help thinking that, if this were done today, it would take a lot longer to build, it would be grim, grey concrete, and there's no way the bean counters would allow something with such excess capacity to be constructed. It would be a pared-back system, with barely capacity enough for the next 25 years.

Parts of Crossness, it has to be said, are very much still under construction. To make access easier in future, a new pathway is being built which avoids the need to cross the Thames Water sewage works, and the garden outside is still in its earliest stages. The main part of the building is accessible, though of course you won't be able to get up to view the top of the engines.

It will also, of course, be a little easier to reach when Crossrail opens, making the journey to Abbey Wood far faster. For now, it's half an hour from Cannon Street, or a DLR to Woolwich Arsenal and then a change of train. While you're in that part of London, besides the various attractions at Greenwich, other things worth a visit include Eltham Palace, Severndroog Castle and the Royal Arsenal at Woolwich.

Visiting on a day when the engines are steaming isn't all you can do at Crossness. My guide, Mike Jones, explained that they always need volunteers. Many of those in the past have been active in the areas immediately useful to the project – working on the restoration of engines, painting the ironwork, and so on. But with work progressing on the new visitor facilities, they'll also need more customer service volunteers, tour guides, people to keep the garden in order and much more.

Ultimately, to enable the engines to work more often, there's likely to be a need for more people who can work them, too. You can find out more information about volunteering on the Crossness web site.

GPS
51.506044, 0.133640

Postcode
SE2 9AQ

Getting there
Train: overground to Abbey Wood National Rail. Minibus shuttle from station to Crossness every 30 minutes on steaming days, starting at 10.15am

Entry
Opening times vary, due to ongoing restoration. Check the website for up to date details. Fee: Adults £6, Children £2, under 5 free.

Online resources
www.crossness.org.uk

Spaceguard Centre
Powys

SA Mathieson

Planet killer: ex-army officer's Welsh space-rock mission

Tunguska, Chelyabinsk... Powys

As I approach the Wales-England border, the rolling Herefordshire countryside sharpens into steep hills and narrow valleys. Powys is a county covering a quarter of Wales, but it is home to just 133,000 people, making it the least densely populated area of Britain south of the North Yorkshire moors.

Limited population means few buildings and roads - and therefore lights. With little annoying visual pollution it's a perfect place from which to watch space from a telescope and look for potentially planet-killing asteroids.

I'm travelling to a privately run observatory dedicated to tracking Near Earth Objects (NEOs): it is known on local signs as Canolfan Gwylio'r Gofod – The Spaceguard Centre.

Arguably the best, last hope of Britain and the world, Spaceguard is the inspiration of a single man: an ex-army officer specialising in surface-to-air missiles called Jonathan Tate.

It also turns out to be a fun and absorbing tourist attraction for all the family. Once over the border it's not long before I'm in Knighton – a rare town in the Powys expanse - where I find a brown sign that directs me to the site.

After several minutes' ascent and just as the single-track lane levels out, another sign directs me on to a farm track. Through a farm gate, the summit reveals a collection of red-brick buildings topped off with a lopsided metal cylinder, used to house a large telescope.

At 1,368 feet (417m) above sea level, the Spaceguard Centre would be a fine place to survive the tsunami that would result from a sizeable asteroid hitting the Atlantic, and – given its remote location and good sightlines downhill – a decent place to hole up for the breakdown of civilisation that would probably follow, even in Wales.

The aim of the Spaceguard Centre is to help stop near-earth objects (NEOs) hitting Earth in the first place: in June 2015 Spaceguard participated in Asteroid Day, a global project to raise awareness of asteroids.

Asteroid Day came with a declaration signed by some of the big names of international space and science calling for greater technology to track near-earth asteroids. Among the signatures were those of Professor Brian Cox, Canadian ISS commander astronaut Jill Tarter of the SETI Institute.

As part of Asteroid Day, Spaceguard ran a free open afternoon, but I dropped in before that and was hosted by Tate. The tour is basically a 90-minute interactive lecture by Tate, armed with props including a planetarium, real meteorite samples and a 2.5 ton (2,540kg) telescope. Visitors can ask questions as and when they like: if anyone knows the answer, it is likely to be Tate.

He walks us around the centre's well-equipped exhibition room, using its items to make things clearer. He starts by talking about the formation of stars and planets with the help of a model solar system and a few minutes in a small planetarium, then zeroes in on asteroids and comets – bodies small enough to be wrenched out of a regular solar orbit.

He explains that 100-150 tons (101,605-152,407kg) of material hits the Earth's atmosphere every day: mostly dust, some of which causes shooting stars. Tate is interested in the bigger stuff that either falls to Earth or explodes – or "pops", as he cheerily puts it – in the atmosphere. The NEO that burnt up over Chelyabinsk in Russia in February 2013 was around 65.6ft (20m) across and popped 18.6-25.9 miles (30-45km) up, but it still injured 1,600 people by causing a shockwave which blew out windows.

The largest asteroid impact on Earth in recent history was the 1908 Tunguska event in Siberia, the explosion from which levelled hundreds of square kilometres of forest. If that had taken place over south-east England, it could have demolished London and damaged buildings across the UK. A prehistoric NEO turned 115 square miles (300km^2) of Middle Eastern desert to glass. To illustrate all this, there is a glass case of off-planet samples, which Tate shows to wide-eyed children and grown-ups alike.

Some NEOs would have even more, er, impact. A 0.62 mile (1km) -wide rock would kill a fifth of the Earth's population and set civilisation back to the Middle Ages, at least until surviving *Register* readers were able to rebuild the internet. A collision between Earth and an object 5km wide would cause massive climate change as well as make a very big hole, sending us and much of the rest of life on Earth the way of the dinosaurs – this is probably what wiped them out. Summing up the full range of Earth-bound objects, from harmless shooting stars to the end of life, Tate tells us: "We've got a pretty big toy-box to play with."

First, he provides the good news: the last 20 years have seen around 95 per cent of NEOs more than a kilometre in size spotted and tracked. Their orbits have been calculated, and none are coming this way for at least a century. And it gets better – if and when we spot one that is, there are plenty of ways to move them out of our way.

The nuclear option taken by Bruce Willis in the 1998 film *Armageddon* is not recommended by Tate: blowing up one large, predictable object would produce thousands of unpredictable smaller ones. Far better to nudge the NEO than nuke it, he tells us, as red kites and buzzards wheel outside. We might use ablation – heating up part of the object, causing it to vent vapour so it propels itself like a rocket motor – or park a large spacecraft near the object, exerting enough gravity to shift it away from a collision course.

For a comet that rarely comes close to the Sun, we might only have a couple of years to change its orbit – but most NEOs are asteroids, where humanity should have decades to get organised. "The bottom line is, there is nothing here we can't do," Tate says, adding that the dinosaurs simply lacked a space programme. The bad news is that we aren't putting in the ground work – at least, not enough of it. While astronomers have tabs on most of the biggest NEOs, work has barely started on those that could take out a city. An asteroid of 492ft (150m) would reach the ground at as much as 50,000mph (80,467kph) – triple that if it were a comet – continue into the crust, then explode, causing a crater 1.8mile (3km) wide.

At the end of 2014, NASA's Near Earth Object Programme had 11,949 asteroid NEOs on its database, with just 861 of them larger than a kilometre across. Of those between 459ft (140m) and 0.62 mile (1km), Tate says we probably know of just five per cent to 10 per cent of the total. At the current rate of discovery it could take more than a century to spot and track the rest. But things are looking up. The US is already involved, through NASA's Ames Research Centre and the US Air Force Space Command, with the NEO issue being championed in Washington by US congressman Dana Rohrabacher. The European Space Agency is also increasingly contributing to the field.

So how about Her Majesty's Government? "Doing nothing - not a terribly bright idea, current British government policy," Tate tells us.

In 2000, the UK government commissioned a comprehensive report on NEOs and decided to give the National Space Centre in Leicester £300,000 to build an exhibition and website, designating it as the National Near Earth Objects Information Centre. The Spaceguard Centre recently took over the national information centre job, but is also part of the global effort to track NEOs. Spaceguard itself is a classic product of British inspiration and inertia: Tate proposed back in 1996 that the Ministry of Defence establish a centre to study the threat posed to the UK by the impact of an asteroid or comet.

He claimed support from Arthur C Clarke and scientists including Gene Schoemaker – who helped discover comet Comet Shoemaker–Levy 9 which broke up and collided with Jupiter in 1994 – and Professor Edward Teller, who was an early member of the Manhattan Project which developed the atomic bomb in the US.

The MoD passed on his proposal, but not the Department of Trade and Industry, which funded further study and established a task force to assess the threat. That study led to nothing much happening, so Tate set up the Spaceguard Centre, opened in 2001 by Sir Patrick Moore. It was equipped with private money, although it received a £1,400 award from the Particle Physics and Astronomy Research Council (PPARC) in 2002.

Spaceguard is today home to two large, robotically-controlled telescopes, used by Tate to confirm other people's NEO spottings. Moving us across to his control centre, he demonstrates the process: a progression through three time-separated images of the same patch of the night sky where an NEO is expected, which makes it easy to spot what's moving. Software automatically prepares reports for the International Astronomical Union's Minor Planets Center, helping to calculate orbits.

As a finale, Tate leads us out of the exhibition room into the tall circular space which houses one of these two telescopes. After climbing some steps, we see a 13-inch (33cm) lens, 2.5-ton (2,540kg) refractor telescope on a hydraulically powered floor – which Tate demonstrates while we're standing on it – and a rotating roof. Another 14-inch (35.5cm) lens telescope sits inside a white dome opposite the observatory's car park, although this isn't part of the tour.

It all sounds a little Bond villainesque, as does the centre's Project Drax, named after Moonraker's missile-obsessed baddie. Having said that, most

Bond villain projects don't include "possibly the survival of the human species" in an online mission statement – but Project Drax does, because all being well, it will let Tate search for new NEOs, as well as confirm those already seen.

Back down the stairs, he shows off pictures of the telescope he will use under Project Drax. In June 2009, the Spaceguard Centre took ownership of a 24-inch (60.9cm) lens, 7.5 ton (7,620kg) Schmidt Camera, built in Newcastle in 1950 and later moved from Cambridge to Knighton. It was donated by Cambridge University's Institute of Astronomy, as light pollution in Cambridgeshire meant it was no longer viable. When it is installed in dark-sky Powys, it will be the largest telescope in Wales, capable of observing five degrees of sky at a time.

Since then, Tate and a group of volunteers have largely built the housing for the new telescope and installed its base assembly: visitors can see this to the right of the centre's entrance. To install the telescope itself – currently waiting shrink-wrapped in plastic – and the technology to work it, the Spaceguard Centre needs the final third of the project's £97,000 budget.

If money were no object, Tate reckons work could be finished within months. But now, our tour exits through the gift shop – because this, along with donations and entrance fees, is how the Spaceguard Centre is raising the rest of the money to set up what will be the only dedicated asteroid tracker outside of the United States.

Tate encourages us to dig deep, not least because he has stationed a sniper outside to take out non-payers. He's probably joking.

The location of the centre on top of a hill in a remote part of the country means that getting here is likely to take a bit of planning. There is no catering on-site, although there are cafes and inns including the Horse and Jockey down in Knighton. The town also offers the Offa's Dyke Centre, a museum about the giant earthwork which marked the old border between Wales and England and the long-distance path that now follows it. Other nearby attractions include the scenic Elan Valley estate further into Powys, the Red Kite feeding station near Rhayader and the Small Breeds Farm Park and Owl Centre in Kington in Herefordshire.

Knighton, which also has a branchline train station, is just 17 miles (27km) west of the handsome and historic town of Ludlow, a tourist favourite. It is also less than 75 miles (120km) from population centres including Birmingham, Stoke-on-Trent and Cheltenham.

It's worth allowing some extra time to get to the Spaceguard Centre, as the local roads are more scenic than speedy. But it is worth the trip. Visitors learn about the problem of NEOs from someone who devotes his life to the subject and can explain it in an informative and drily humorous fashion in a way that isn't likely to scare children - although it may confirm adults' fears about the UK government.

And by paying to visit, you also become a small part of the solution.

GPS
52.325, -3.019

Postcode
LD7 1LW

Getting there
By car: Knighton is on the A4113 from Ludlow and the A488 from Llandrindod Wells to Shrewsbury. The Spaceguard Centre is reached by turning off the A4113 just east of the town centre, and driving south (and up) Llanshay Lane for 1.5 miles, then west on a farm track. There are clear signs at each junction, which are to be trusted more than your satnav. Public transport: Knighton train station is about 50 minutes from Shrewsbury on a stopping service which runs four times each weekday and reaches Swansea three hours later. You will then have a long walk uphill to the Spaceguard Centre – it may be better to get a cab.

Entry
Entry is by conducted tour only, and costs £7 for adults, £4 for children aged 5 to 15. Tours run on Wednesdays, Thursday, Fridays, Saturdays and Sundays at 2pm and 4pm from October to April, and also at 10.30am from May to September. Although it is usually possible to turn up at one of these times on spec, the centre recommends you phone first in case it has a block booking. Group tours can be arranged at any time (including evenings, for £1 extra per person), with a minimum charge of £48.

Online resources
www.spaceguardcentre.com/
www.visitknighton.co.uk/

Thames Barrier
London

Gavin Clarke

The Great Barrier Relief – inside London's heavy metal and concrete defence act

Waves against the machine

Last time London flooded was 1953. Three hundred lives were lost, 30,000 evacuated and the damage totalled a considerable £5bn in today's money.

Given how London has expanded since then, the record-breaking wet winter of 2014 would have been worse had it not been for the presence of 51,000 tons (51,818,392kg) of metal and 7,416,080ft^3 (210,000m^3) of concrete – called the Thames Barrier.

The barrier has been raised 174 times in the 35 years of its life: and 50 of those took place during that three-month period of 2014.

That year saw one of the wettest winters since records began in 1766 – 435mm of rain, beating incumbent 1915 on 423mm, with the flood walls of 1953 that breached still in place. The barrier added a crucial extra three metres to their height.

Without that, a 48 mile^2 (125km^2) -area of London was at risk: historical landmarks, commercial and residential buildings, and underground lines and stations in a city that contributes £250bn to the UK's economy.

The Thames is not unique in having a flood defence system. Other big cities and waterways have them, too, with at least six in Northern Europe: Venice, Holland and St Petersburg all have various systems. There's a further eight systems on the Thames across tributaries that – with the Thames Barrier – are links in London's flood-defence chain.

Where the Thames Barrier stands out is in its marriage of forward-thinking design with innovative, yet practical, engineering. It's not the biggest flood barrier in the world, but it isthe largest moveable barrier.

The secret was a new floodgate design – the rising-sector gate conceived by those designing the barrier – that's both powerful enough to withstand nearly ten thousand tons of water pressure yet wide enough for commercial and leisure craft to pass through into, and out of, London.

The barrier's gates rely on a simple system of industrial plant with multiple levels of redundancy. In a nightmare scenario of lost power and computers, it is possible to operate the gates manually out on the barrier.

Then there's that look. Bigger barriers in St Petersburg and Holland are testament to their municipal roots or practical purpose: squat concrete cubes or guillotine gates serving as bulwarks against angry Mother Nature.

The Thames Barrier's signature is a set of seven, silver-coloured domes on boat-shaped piers that straddle the river and resemble a fleet of yachts with the wind behind them, in flight into the centre of London.

These domes and piers might well serve a practical purpose by housing the barrier's machinery from the elements, but they have also earned iconic status. Any picture of the London skyline that includes Nelson's Column, Tower Bridge and St Paul's is incomplete without the Thames Barrier.

I survey this sight from my vantage point high in the barrier's control room. I'm clutching a blue hard hat as I'll be out there in a few minutes, descending walkways, and squeezing past gears and pistons on a journey through this water-control machine and under the Thames to pier number seven.

It's a brisk and breezy December afternoon when I visit. Daylight is waning with Canary Wharf and the O2 receding in purple gloom and a banshee wind screeching around the piers. I feel like Ripley and the Colonial Marines in the terraformer on LV-426.

Compounding this is the secure feel of this facility. The control room on the south bank tops a tower in the middle of a small complex containing a power station and workshops and protected by stout walls, heavy gates and a very taking-no-chances pillbox-like entry point. It's testament to the barrier's status as a piece of critical national infrastructure.

Inside the control room, however, all is calm (mundane even) with barely a handful of staff visible. The presence of flat-screen monitors, workstations and carpet makes it feel rather office-like, albeit an office with a commanding view. There's glass on three sides: to the left the City, ahead the north bank's tower blocks, and to the east the Woolwich Ferry and beyond.

But don't be fooled. Everything is arranged with purpose like the bridge of a ship, or the USS Enterprise, even. This bridge is split into distinct areas of activity: on one side weather monitoring, opposite are systems that raise and lower the gates, across the back run desks and phones where supervisors filter incoming data and assess whether to close the gates. In the far corner is comms who relay to the world any decision to raise or lower the flood control gates spanning the Thames.

Along the back is a schematic of the barrier, showing walkways and power lines.

Thames tidal defence operations manager Andy Batchelor is my guide. Batchelor is one of those who'd sit on that desk at the back, and who's authorized to give the order to open and close the barrier. He's been working here since 1984, when it was officially opened by HM the Queen and Prince Philip.

Batchelor's position is high pressure: yes, closing the barrier has the potential to save London and her people but getting it wrong would also be a disaster, if of different proportions.

"We've got to be certain of what we are doing to minimise the disruption," Batchelor tells me. "It's got to be based on the information, and there's no medals for getting this wrong."

The Port of London, with offices on the opposite bank, annually contributes £3.4bn to the national economy. Ships passing through the barrier to the Port of London handle 50 million tons of goods and 70 independent wharfs and terminals along 95 miles (152km) of water. When the barrier goes up, that lot comes to a halt. That network of other barriers along the Thames would close, too.

If the gates close, Batchelor's team must get on the phone to the Port of London Authority, London Transport, emergency services, local authorities, the Woolwich Ferry, plus 36 other floodgates and 400 smaller structures that comprise a flood-defence ring with the barrier, including the Dartford Barrier and Tilbury Dock.

The barrier gets the attention but it couldn't work on its own. "People get confused – they think it's just the Thames Barrier that's doing the job – it's the complete system, it's like a chain. Take out one of the links and you will have flooding," Batchelor said.

Any decision to operate the thousands of tons of machinery sitting out there in the river is based on an expert reading of incoming data from weather forecasts and situations on the ground. Data read-outs are displayed on a bank of flat monitors, currently displaying wiggly coloured lines.

Some of the feeds come from five-day ensemble forecasts crunched by Met Office's supercomputers in Exeter. Ensemble forecasts give you not one but a variety of results based on different factors. Forecasts are run for three days, to give greater detail.

The results are mapped against knowns, such as scheduled sea tides and fluvial flow up the river. Forecasts are supplemented with data from monitors ranging from up in the North Sea to Teddington Weir in South-West London, the last tidal point on the Thames.

The team sifts for signs of surges mixed with a high tide and low-pressure in the North Sea – the fatal mix of 1953. They look, too, for any excess rain running off land into the river, as occurred in 2014.

Closure is triggered when a combination of high-tide forecasts in the North Sea and high-river flows at Teddington Weir – 22 miles (35km) from here – indicate water levels would exceed 15.9ft (4.87m) in central London.

In Winter 2014, the barrier closed nine times because of tidal surges and on 41 occasions because of high river flow, essentially water running off into the Thames.

The strategy was to raise the barrier's gates after low tide to stop water coming back upstream from the North Sea, thereby creating an empty reservoir behind the gates. Run-off from the land would fill this reservoir so that, rather than hit a wall of tidal inflow from the North Sea, it could be released in a controlled way after the next high tide.

Coming back to the now, Batchelor points to a bulge of coloured lines on one screen: it represents a tidal surge as recorded by various tidal markers at different points along the North East coast.

Things are quiet today but in Winter 2014 it was different: 1,341.9ft^3 (38m^3) of water a second were flowing over that Teddington tidal outpost. The weekend before my trip was wet, 3,531.4ft (100m^3) a second. January to March 2014 hit 18,893ft^3 (535m^3) per second, although history records even bigger numbers, up to 28,251.7ft^3 (800m^3) in 1894. However, these lasted for just a few days.

Directly opposite us on this bridge are the systems responsible for the remote control of those gates down in the river. When it unofficially opened in 1982, the operations centre resembled the control room of a power station that was full of levers and knobs and dials.

Instructions to the barrier's gates were sent via thousands of relays. The only computers were a VAX running PDP 11 for forecasting and a Commodore Pet with a five-and-a-quarter-inch floppy drive that ran planned maintenance.

The Bakelite and white-coat era systems were phased out in the 1990s, for the first PC-based systems controlled via custom keyboards.

Today, it's Windows 7 PCs and Windows Server 2008 R2 systems that talk to the industrial plan on the barrier's piers to raise and lower the gates. The network and servers are mirrored and a RAID 6 blade server with several terabytes of storage records every piece of data generated.

These computers control a system of moving gates that are unique.

The Eastern Scheldt, south-west Netherlands, and the St Petersburg flood barrier use concrete piers, sluices and dams while the barrier in Venice is tripped automatically. Permanent defences couldn't have worked on the Thames because of the river's importance to all that commerce going in and out of the Port of London; it would have blocked ships. A system tripped by tidal pressure was impossible because of the variance of rainfall that the UK receives and the fact the Thames has a tidal range of seven metres.

The systems up here control six rising sector gates in the centre of the river and a further four falling radial gates sitting on the shallow north and south banks. Instructions are relayed to a plant that does the lifting on nine concrete piers, seven of which are topped by those silver-coloured shells.

A single engineer could, in theory, operate all the barrier's gates but in practice there are always two on duty, as operating the gates isn't as simple as clicking "OK" on a screen dialogue. You need to step through a series of sequenced and connected moves beginning with turning on power packs that control a series of arms and levers out on those islands responsible for raising and lowering the gates. This is done gate by gate.

Parameters must be satisfied, such as packs running, the correct selections made, direction (open or closed), selection of the correct gate, and so on.

On my trip I met one of those whose jobs it is to operate the gates, control-room shift engineer Tony Davies. "Tony has the intellect to know what to do if we need to run down that series of circumstances," Batchelor tells me. There are different ways to close the gates; using the main control and local, using duty and stand-by power pack, or manually on the barrier should systems up here fail and should there be a major power outage. There are monthly test closures, with gates operated once a fortnight.

"On those, we go through all those options. If we didn't, well, we are all creatures of habit and would do it one way. It's my way of doing QA," Batchelor said.

"We need Tony as an engineer to know what it is he's pressing, so he's not just following a script. We need to have his intelligence to know that when, say, we come to step number five what number five does rather than moving onto number six," Batchelor told us.

The flight desk Tony pilots is sacrosanct: there's no internet connection and – sorry codeheads – no upgrades or fiddling on live systems in case bugs are introduced. This system hasn't been touched in four years with changes only made when there's a systems upgrade or the need for a re-think.

Arguably the biggest change was the switch to computers in the 1990s with the move away from Bakelite and thousands of relays. A computerised system based on those used in oil exploration in the North Sea was constructed using custom keyboards and controls that evolved into a supervisory control and data acquisition (SCADA) system of standard mouse and keyboard UI.

Today it's a custom-built point and click interface. Opening the gate involves satisfying a series of logical sequences, from getting power packs running through to moving those gates, one at a time. Closing each gate takes 15 minutes and shutting the lot takes an hour and a half.

Change is in the wind for this lot: the plant out in the piers is being replaced while the ageing control-room software is ready for an update. A pilot is underway looking at "tighter integration" and use of Windows Server 2012.

The juice for this lot, meanwhile, comes courtesy of the National Grid: two sources on the north and the south bank for redundancy plus there's a trio of 1.5MW generators on site and a rotary flywheel that serves as a UPS in the event of a blackout and ensures uninterrupted supply during any outages.

The flywheel replaced hundreds of batteries and ensures uninterrupted supply during a total loss of mains power. There have been six blackouts in South East England during the barrier's history.

But, hey, I'm not holding a hard hat for the fun of it: it's time to get out on the barrier.

I leave the control room with Batchelor and we descend to ground level via an aluminium lift, pause for a reading of the health and safety rules before Batchelor pushes the bar on what looks like a fire-escape and next thing I can barely hear myself think for the wind ripping past my ears.

We traverse a walkway over the first falling sector gate, over a muddy bank and enter a door in the side of one of those silver-coloured domes, before descending the first of a series of glossy grey metal gantries and stairways en route to our destination: pier number seven.

The Thames Barrier looks big enough from the outside, spanning half a kilometre of water, with each concrete pier eight times longer, five times wider and four times higher than a traditional London double-decker bus. Each silver roof peaks at six times the height of a modern two-storey house.

But this is an iceberg and it's only inside you grasp the enormity of things: we clank across gantries and down stairways heading 18 metres below water level into the muddy bed of the river and the barrier's base.

Each pier comprises 1,808,336.9ft^2 (168,000m^2) of concrete while the sill is made of a further 355,209ft^2 (33,000m^2). Two service tunnels run through the sill; these let you traverse the barrier and connect each of the piers.

Remarkably, while the concrete was poured during the 1970s, things still look fresh and you'd never guess you were underwater: there's no dripping pools gathering on the floor and no mineral excretion squeezing through walls. Rather, the concrete walls and floor have an eggshell glaze, rows of orange cables hurry along walls and high-viz signs point their way to the various decks and walkways. It even smells clean, apart from one area of the tunnel dominated by a damp dish-cloth smell as we pass through, the result of engineers flushing old oil through the system.

We hit the bottom, and we're in one of two service tunnels. The sill contains a concave recess to house the rising sector gates when open, thereby allowing shipping to continue to pass unobstructed overhead. This sill is 18 metres deep and sits 27.8ft (8.5m) deep in the riverbed; there are two metres of concrete above my head. Beneath my feet, 88.5ft (27m) of foundation.

Along one wall run pipes carrying oil and the fire suppression system while

the other holds power lines, carrying up to 1,100 volts, and data cables, with copper being replaced by fibre. In the floor, drains run beneath metal covers.

It's as good a place as any to take stock, in the gloom and artificial light.

Floods are a feature of life on the Thames going back the full 1,500 years of human settlement around the river, but 1953 was the worst recorded in terms of sheer losses. However, things only kicked off following a 1967 review in the wake of yet more flooding, this time in the German city of Hamburg, and the Thames Barrier Act was passed by Parliament in 1972.

Next job was barrier design – something that hung in the balance for some time. The government ruled the barrier must be reliable, compatible with tidal flows, navigable and appealing to the eye.

Designers Rendel, Palmer & Tritton (today HPR) proposed a guillotine-like drop-gate with two large openings in 1958 but this was rejected as were a pair of 150-metre wide openings favoured by Port of London.

Rendel, Palmer & Tritton evaluated 10 sites and 41 different plans with various options rejected either for not being navigable or for being visually offensive. The breakthrough came in 1969 when the company's engineer, Charles Draper, conceived the rising sector gate, reputedly inspired by the domestic gas valve. The design ticked all the government's boxes and construction started in 1974.

The rising sector gates look, in profile, like semi-circles. When not in use they lie flat side up in the concrete sills making the route between the piers navigable for shipping of most commercial and military size.

The gates rotate on a trunnion shaft attached to a concrete pier on either side, lifted by a jointed arm and powered by the industrial plant inside each pier and sheltered beneath those silver-coloured domes.

As for the site, Woolwich Reach, this was selected for its narrow width and firm foundations, being of solid chalk.

Construction spanned 18-plus contractors and eight years, and involved digging and dredging channels and the sinking of coffer dams driven to depths of up to 78.7ft (24m) into the river bed. The concrete piers, the base of those silver roofs, were sunk first; the sills were built using a mix of concrete reinforced with steel.

They were built in a specially constructed dry dock on the north bank that was flooded so they could be floated out and lowered into position. It was a finely choreographed ballet that involved tugs and specially designed heavy-duty beams and synchronised winches from Sparrows Contract Services. Precision was paramount: the biggest sills are 196.8ft (60m) long by 88.5ft (27m) wide, and 27.8ft (8.5m) high — oh yeah, and weigh 9,000 tons

(9,144,422kg). Units had to be moved in a confined space in fast-flowing water and positioned on the river bed 52ft (16m) below to an accuracy of within 10mm.

Apart from the metal gates, which were unique construction, every piece of machinery that was used to power the raising and closing of the gates had already been proved in the field elsewhere, according to Batchelor.

But the barrier didn't just challenge the engineering brains: it shook up labour relations and financing, too.

The project initially used 12-hour shifts of workers – a common practice in civil engineering, but alien to a local labour force more accustomed to a 40-hour week. A switch to three, eight-hour shifts produced resentment, caused by loss of overtime pay.

The length of the project combined with the uncertain economic climate of the 1970s and early 1980s (up to 24 per cent inflation) meant contractors wouldn't agree to a fixed-price contract. Funding was finally split between the government, 75 per cent, and the customer, the Greater London Council (GLC) which covered 25 per cent of the bill that landed at £535m (roughly £1.8bn in today's money.)

After a brief stop to consider this and stroll down the service tunnel we reach a sign to pier seven – time to ascend. Clattering upwards and crossing ante-rooms we break into the daylight, and that screaming wind. Each central pier is 50 metres tall, penetrating the riverbed to 15 metres, is 11 metres wide and 65 metres long.

It's a minimalistic business out here: the pier is boat shaped, with a yellow crane stationed in the middle, like a sail boom. At one end of this pier, a large equipment room; at the other a smaller local control room where engineers can operate a shift and latch system to move the gate should they have to.

The cranes are used to lift the equipment inside and below up and out for repair – there's one on each pier.

Tucked away just to one side is what looks like a yellow elbow joint: it's one of a pair of hydraulic-powered arms 78.7ft (24m) in diameter attached to the rising sector gate. Mostly only one arm is required but, in exceptional circumstances, two could be used.

These gates were built in the North of England and barged down the coast to London. The largest sector gate has a navigable width of 61 metres (equivalent to the aperture at Tower Bridge up-stream) while the smallest rising sector and the radial gates near the banks are not navigable for boats or ships.

The 200ft (61m) gates weigh 3,300 tons (3,352,995kg), of which 50 is paint and another 20 are anodes applied to prevent corrosion to the metal. Each gate is hollow, made of plates 40mm thick and capable of holding back 9,000 tons (9,144,422kg) of water during a tidal surge.

There's a 200mm gap between gate and sill in the riverbed, shrinking to 75mm. The gap between each gate and the sill means that any obstruction would get jet washed through – when closed, the water velocity under the gate reaches 13m/s. The obvious question: what about other possible blockages, such as supermarket trolleys? Faced with the combined power of hydraulics and gate, such a trolley would be mincemeat, Batchelor assures me.

We retreat from the wind-blasted deck to the larger of the pier's two silver structures. Inside is not what you'd expect: equipment, yes, but big equipment; those electric pumps that pull 190 horsepower, operating cylinders, power packs, hooks and chains, some painted in the same juicy yellow as the plant outside.

Gear in here is duplicated, so each gate can be closed by any one of its two duty and stand-by power packs. The machinery is capable of producing a total of 8,000 tons (8,128,375kg) of thrust to move the gates.

Everything is ensconced snugly beneath a delicate high-arched roof built using Iroko beams and European pine planks that help comprise a three-layer skin. The look and resin smell lends things a Scandinavian touch. The barrier's signature stainless-steel tiles are on the outside.

The whole forms more than just an iconic statement – it's practical: the tiles haven't been cleaned in 30 years nor have they been replaced.

This was a real breakthrough: the piers could easily have ended up flat, like the stumps of the Eastern Scheldt barrier, with a road across the top.

"At the time stainless steel, as today, was very expensive, but we've never had to clean it or renew it," Batchelor said. "I'm a civil engineer, and if I'd put a flat roof on it, I'd probably have had to change that a couple of times... it might have taken a little more outlay at the front, but over the term it's saved on cost."

One last thing to see: down and into a narrow side chamber housing a single piece of gear that looks like a piece of massive drill: an 11-foot screw shaft, black with grease and with a series of levers at one end. This is a giant handbreak that grabs the gate and lets you hold it in position while decompressing the hydraulics. In the event of a total hydraulic failure, operators could also use this to lift the gate from the water.

Having squeezed down the side of this giant screw with controls it's time to leave: exit is quicker thanks to a sleek elevator taking us 17 metres back up and out into the fresh and powerfully battering air whipping around outside. On our way Batchelor makes a small confession – he used to get lost down there, in that kilometre of tunnel and among the walkways. "There was no signage or anything," he says.

There's a big fish we haven't gutted: climate change. Or, rather, how can a flood defence more than 40-years old stand up to today's realities of rising sea levels and human development that were, arguably, neither existent nor anticipated at the time? The barrier's end of life was pegged at 2030.

Batchelor cites a report from the Environment Agency (which runs the barrier) called the Thames Estuary 2100 plan that gives the facility a role until at least 2070 based on current assumptions about rising sea levels.

TE2100 recommends the flood defence chain, of which the barrier is a large part, be actively maintained and improved at a cost of £1.2bn, but advocates the need for a long-term decision in 2050 on what comes after 2070. One option on the table - a new barrier at Long Reach in Dartford, six miles away.

TE2100 was the product of six years' research into how flood risk in the tidal Thames floodplain that runs from Teddington to Sheerness and Shoeburyness would change as the result of human development and climate change. This floodplain spans an area of 135 miles^2 (350km^2) and encompasses 1.25m residents, 500,000 homes and 40,000 businesses.

"On current levels we will still be OK," Batchelor said. "Tony will have to keep doing his computer upgrades, the maintenance will keep carrying on, but on current climate predications and forecasts we should be OK to then."

I return my hard hat, shake hands with Batchelor and find myself once more beyond the stone and steel defences. There's time for a look back at the span and wander the short distance to the Thames Barrier Information Centre and café.

You can't pass through the guts of the beast, but you can marvel from the outside walking down that bank. The Thames Barrier is a landmark on at least two walks – the 180-mile (289.6km) Thames Path and the shorter Green Chain Walk – and it can be viewed from the water from a number of tourist and regular riverboats, too.

Surrounding is a mix of commercial and residential, but head south on the Green Chain Walk and you pass through woods once popular with highwaymen leading up to Charlton House and Park. Or you can go north via the Woolwich foot tunnel or ferry: four miles east is Woolwich Royal Arsenal while to the west is Greenwich and all its attractions.

Further out, the towers and bright lights of central London, receding into the purple winter dusk with their lights twinkling. Buildings that owe not just their dry feet but their viability to the machinery I've just seen.

GPS
51.494758, 0.037236

Post Code
SE18 5NJ

Getting there
Car: A206, then on to Eastmoor Street. Car parking available on site. Undergound: North Greenwich, plus two-mile walk. Rail: Charlton or Woolwich Dockyard, plus a short walk.

Entry
Not open to the public.

Online resources
www.gov.uk/the-thames-barrier
www.thames-path.org.uk
https://tfl.gov.uk/modes/walking/green-chain-walk

Our Writers

Gavin Clarke

Gavin's been covering tech since the mid 1990s in Silicon Valley – where he lived for 10 years – and in the UK. He's charted the rise of the new, demise of the old and interviewed the pioneers and power brokers of business and personal computing.

Dominic Connor

A regular columnist and host of *Register* CIO round tables, Dominic has spent his tech career bossing IT pros and quants around major financial institutions. With a background in programming and recruitment, Dominic also lectures on C++ and is chairman of networking group The Real Time Club.

Bob Dormon

Bob is a music technology guru and consumer tech specialist. Before serving as *The Register's* features editor, Bob's skills were employed in a number of fields including music and video production – working with leading artists - and for the spooks of GCHQ.

Joe Fay

Joe has been a tech journo since the 1990s serving in various news roles at *Computerwire, Microscope Magazine* and *The Register*. Now group editor, Joe runs *The Reg's* popular CIO and lecture series for readers and our conference program.

SA Mathieson

SA Mathieson has written about IT since the last millennium for titles including *The Register, The Guardian, Computer Weekly* and *Government Computing*. He is the author of *Card declined: How Britain said no to ID cards, three times over.*

Ed Moore

Ed is director of Ocasta Studios, providing business development, support and consultancy. An experienced technology entrepreneur, Ed's spent his career building companies and start-ups; he's also served at the Bank of England, GEC Avionics and as chief technology officer for Carphone Warehouse Group.

Brid-Aine Parnell

A technology, science and business journalist Brid-Aine's worked for Middle East publications *Arabian Computer News* and *7DAYS*, for *The Register, The Times* and *Forbes.com* where she has covered datacentres, the Internet of Things, patent lawsuits and fintech. Currently a freelancer, Brid-Aine's field also includes astronomy, astrophysics, robotics and space exploration.

Bill Ray

An accomplished freelance writer and wireless engineer, Bill has worked deep in telecoms for some of the biggest names in the operator field at a technical level. Bill's written two books on mobile application development and has cultivated a keen interest in embedded, wireless and Internet of Things.

Tony Smith

Tech writer at Internet of Things' developer Electric Imp, Tony has 25 years as a journalist under his belt writing about consumer, business, product development and research. Tony's served in senior editorial posts on *MicrosScope, The Mac* and *The Register*, and he contributes to *The Sunday Times'* Don't Panic reader Q&A column.

Nigel Whitfield

Nigel is a freelance writer and editor. He counters his enthusiasm for shiny new technology by driving a Citröen DS and developing his own films, and is just as happy writing about weird places as about digital TV.

Dave Wilby

Dave is a professional writer and editor with nearly 20 years of experience authoring and managing creative projects online and off. He has spent much of his career covering the global technology industry, but also works in engineering, healthcare, telecommunications and the environmental sector. Although many of the cutting-edge products he once reviewed can now be found in science museums, Dave definitely still knows his ARP from his ALU.

Lightning Source UK Ltd.
Milton Keynes UK
UKRC02n2200241117
313309UK00001B/47